6th Grade
Winning The Race

by Cherie Noel

Positive Action Bible Curriculum

6th Grade: Winning The Race

First Edition Published 1990
Second Edition Published 2006

Third Printing 2010

Printed in the United States of America

ISBN: 978-1-59557-067-3

Author: Cherie Noel
Curriculum Consultant: Helen Boen
Layout and Design: Shannon Brown

Contents

Unit One: Preparing For The Race

1	The Greatest Book Ever Written	7
2	Josiah—The King With Character	11
3	God Speaks	15

Unit Two: Developing Inner Strength

4	God's Design For Me	21
5	God's Purpose For Me	27
6	Being Filled With The Spirit	31
7	Finding True Joy	37
8	When A Christian Sins	41

Unit Three: Striving For The Prize

9	Being In God's Will	47
10	Honoring Your Parents	51
11	Reputation And Character	57
12	God Wants Your Heart	61
13	Learning To Stand Alone	65
14	Dare To Stand	69

Unit Four: Hindrances To The Runner

15	Acting Like A Fool	75
16	Greed And Covetousness	79
17	Your Enemy, The Devil	83
18	How Satan Tempts Us	87
19	Overcoming Temptation	93
20	Conformity To Christ	99
21	Separation From Worldliness	103

Unit Five: Pressing Toward The Goal

22	The Lamb Of God	109
23	The Miracles Of Christ	113
24	Christ Shows Us How To Live	117
25	Christ-Like Attitudes	123
26	The Crucifixion	127
27	The Resurrection	131
28	Power For Christian Living	135

Unit Six: The Prize Is Won

29	What Will Happen In The Future?	141
30	Christ Returns For His Own	145
31	The Tribulation	149
32	The Antichrist	153
33	Christ Returns And Reigns	157
34	The Final Judgment	161
35	Review Of Revelation	165

| | Music Curriculum | 171 |
| | Scripture Memorization Sheet | 187 |

Unit One:
Preparing For The Race

Every four years the world takes particular note of a very special event—the Olympic games. The Olympics are held in different countries around the world, and athletes from all the countries of the world compete against each other for gold, silver, and bronze medals. To be an Olympic athlete is a great achievement. To win a medal is one of the world's great honors.

Those who compete in the Olympic games must train and prepare for many years. Preparation for this competition is unlike any other because these athletes practice many hours a day for years in order to be ready for the competition.

One reason the Olympics are not held more often than every four years is because the athletes must be well prepared and trained. Training and participation in smaller competitions to win a place on the Olympic teams requires extra effort for the athlete.

The decathlon is the most difficult competition of all, and the participants in this event are the greatest of all athletes. "Decathlon" means ten events. Athletes who take part must train for all ten events and therefore cannot focus on just one competition. The variety of the events requires competitors to be well-rounded in their physical strength and speed, not merely specialists in one particular skill.

To become a strong Christian requires the same inner determination and strength of character as is required of such athletes as these. The preparation for the Christian is found in the Word of God as God lays the foundation for the victory. As the Christian studies, absorbs, and spends time in God's Word, he will be prepared to be victorious in life. Just as the athlete competes, so must we compete against forces outside of ourselves that want to overcome and defeat us.

As we study the Bible this year, we will see how the Christian life is similar to a great race. The Bible makes many references to the race we run as Christians and to the victory that Jesus Christ can give us. But it all starts with preparation from the Word of God.

LESSON 1
The Greatest Book Ever Written

Key Verse: Ephesians 6:17

VOCABULARY

Prophet: a spokesman for God who uttered the exact words the Lord gave him

Prophecy: something said by a prophet that reveals the divine will of God; a warning of something to come; a vivid, pointed, solemn prediction

Doctrine: a principle held as divine truth

Inspiration: the special influence of the Holy Spirit guiding certain persons to speak and write what God wanted communicated to others

Rebuking: blame or censure for a misdeed; a mild reproof or scolding

Righteousness: actions judged as proper by the standards of God's holy law, which is derived from His holy character

The Bible is the greatest book that has ever been written. In it God Himself speaks to men. It is a book of divine instruction. The Bible is not simply one book. It is an entire library of books that contain a wide variety of information, but it is tied together by one central purpose. The Bible was written by dozens of authors over a period of 1,600 years. It was written in three languages on three continents. The authors were poets, educators, singers, princes, kings, fishermen, and statesmen. Some of these authors were great scholars, while others were unlearned and ignorant men.

The Written Word And The Living Word

It would seem that with this many authors, the individual pieces of the Bible would not fit together well. Yet there is great unity throughout the book because really there was only one Author. To understand how so many authors could be unified in their writing of one book, we need to understand that there really was only one main Author.

Read 2 Peter 1:21 and explain in your own words how a book written by so many different people could be unified into the Word of God. _____

_____

_____

_____

The Word of God was authored by God Himself. The great subject of God's Word is the Lord Jesus Christ. The person and work of Jesus Christ are promised, prophesied, and pictured in the Old Testament. The life of the Lord Jesus is revealed in the four Gospels, and the meaning and purpose of His life, death, and resurrection are explained in the Epistles. His expected return is foretold in the book of Revelation.

Therefore, the great purpose of the written Word of God, the Bible, is to reveal the living Word of God, the Lord Jesus Christ. God explains this in John 1:1–18. Read and study this passage and then answer the following questions:

What three statements are made about the Word in John 1:1?

1. _____

2. _____

3. _____

What does verse 14 mean when it says that the Word became flesh? _____

_____

Why do we capitalize the name "Word"? _____

_____

List the various ways John describes Jesus in verses 3, 4, and 9.

• _____

• _____

• _____

What does John say about who Jesus was and how the world accepted Him?

• Verse 10: _____

_____.

• Verse 11: _____

_____.

What is the central message of the Bible (vs. 12)? _____

_____

_____

✎ According to verse 18, how then can we "see" God? _____

_____

Life Principle: Jesus Christ (the living Word) is the true God. The Bible (the written Word), though written by dozens of different people, actually has only one Author—God Himself.

✎ We therefore know some very important facts about the Word of God and its Author. Some of these facts are listed below. See how many of the following blanks you can complete with the correct word:

- Jesus is G_____.

- Jesus was the C_____ of the universe.

- The W_____ has always existed with God.

- God used d_____ of different men to put His Word into w_____ form.

- The H_____ S_____ worked through men to write down God's Word for us.

- The Bible is the w_____ W_____ of God.

- Jesus Christ is the l_____ W_____ of God.

Purposes For Studying God's Word

✎ Second Timothy 3:16 gives four reasons for us to study God's Word. List the four purposes below as given in this verse. Beside each purpose, look up the word in the dictionary and write the definition. We need to make sure we understand the purposes for studying God's Word.

1. _____

   _____

2. _____

   _____

3. _____

   _____

4. _____

   _____

   _____

The Bible is, therefore, our only way of knowing God personally. Through studying God's Word this year, we will learn more about God, more about God's purpose for our lives, and how to live our lives in such a way as to have God's blessing.

Winning Your Race

Variations of the phrase, "This is what the Lord says," occur hundreds of times in the Old Testament alone. The Bible is truly the Word of God. Never underestimate its importance, uniqueness, or worth!

Give an example of how the Lord could use each of these purposes in your own life (from 2 Tim. 3:16). _____

_____

Name a Bible doctrine (teaching) you learned this week.

_____

_____

Name an area in your life that the Lord may need to rebuke through His Word.

_____

_____

Name an area in your life that God may need to correct or change.

_____

_____

Give an example of some training in righteousness God might give you.

_____

_____

LESSON 2
Josiah—The King With Character

Key Verse: Psalm 119:9

We have heard many times how fortunate we are to live in America. Many Christians around the world do not have Bibles. In many countries, reading the Bible is against the law. Sometimes, when we are used to having something that is easily obtained, we forget how special it really is. The Bible is not an ordinary book, and we need to remind ourselves of the privilege we have of possessing one. At no other time in history and in no other country has it been as easy to own a Bible. We are indeed privileged.

We have already discussed how we got our Bible and some of the reasons for studying it. To remind ourselves of the importance of studying God's Word, let's look at some other important verses.

 Read Psalm 119:11. What is a primary purpose for studying His Word? _____
_____

 As we studied in our last lesson, the Bible is a "living" book—it is God-breathed! It knows your mind and heart and can tell you things about yourself of which you might not be aware. Read Psalm 139:23–24 and explain what we should be desiring to see God do in our hearts through His Word.

_____
_____
_____
_____

Josiah's Family

In this lesson we are going to study the story of King Josiah, who became the king of Judah when he was only eight years old. King Josiah has a unique story because the Word of God played a very unique role in his life.

First, we need to see what kind of a family Josiah had. His father's name was Amon. Read about Amon and about Josiah's grandfather, Manasseh, in 2 Chronicles 33:21–24.

 What did Amon and Manasseh do that was wrong in the eyes of the Lord? _____
_____

Describe the character of Amon.

_____

_____

_____

_____

_____

 How did God deal with Amon in verse 24?

_____

_____

_____

_____

_____

_____

Josiah's Character

When Josiah became king, the nation of Judah was very sinful. His father had been a godless man and a terrible leader. When the leadership rebels against God, the nation will have many problems. In this case, the land was full of idols, the temple was falling apart, and the enemies of Judah were getting stronger and stronger.

But Josiah had learned to stand alone and do right. He had to learn these things on his own because he did not have the right kind of parents teaching him or showing him a good example. But Josiah was not led astray by the poor character of his father or the idol-worshiping people in his nation.

 Read 2 Chronicles 34:1–3 and describe the character of Josiah.

_____

_____

_____

Life Principle: Right character produces right actions.

Josiah's Actions

The Bible says that Josiah had an excellent example to follow. He did not imitate the godless men of Judah's history (including his own father).

 Who was Josiah's hero according to 2 Chronicles 34:2–3? _____

The desire of Josiah's heart was to seek after God. The Bible teaches that real faith in God will cause you to do something. Others will know what you think and stand for; they will be able to tell by your actions. King Josiah's faith made him act.

✏ Based on 2 Chronicles 34:3–7, explain what King Josiah did first in the land of Judah. _____

_____

_____

_____

✏ It took Josiah six years to clean up the land. Now he set to work at the next task. According to 2 Chronicles 34:8–13, what did he do next? _____

_____

_____

Do not think that it was easy for Josiah to give his heart to the Lord. It isn't always easy even if you have parents and teachers who love the Lord and show you the right example of Christian character.

It is so much more difficult if parents and friends are constantly pulling you away from the Lord or if your parents are gone, as was true in Josiah's life. But in spite of the idol worship in his land and the sinful character of his father, Josiah was proud to stand for God. Josiah's character is a good example for all of us to follow and learn from, especially since he had the strength to take a strong stand while he was so young. And because he loved the Lord, God was able to use him to reveal His Word once again.

Read the following verses in 2 Chronicles 34 and answer these questions:

✏ Verse 27: What attitude did God see in the heart of Josiah? _____

_____

✏ Verse 28: What did God promise Josiah because his heart was right? _____

_____

_____

✏ Verse 25: Why was God's wrath to be poured out on the people? _____

_____

_____

✏ Verse 30: What need did Josiah see that the people had, and what did he do about it?

_____

_____

Verse 31: Copy the promises Josiah made before the Lord.

- _____

- _____
  _____

- _____

Winning Your Race

God used Josiah and other faithful men and women to lead many people to worship Him.

Whom should we admire more? These people, or God Himself? Why?
_____
_____

Is it your desire to develop the type of character that can be a testimony to others? Why or why not? _____
_____

LESSON 3
God Speaks

Key Verse: Hebrews 4:12

VOCABULARY

Discern: to come to know something that is not clear or easily recognizable to the mind or eye

Zeal: an enthusiastic, often intense interest or devotion to a cause

Zealot: a person who is intensely or fanatically devoted to a cause

When we read the Word of God, the Creator of the universe is actually speaking directly to our hearts and minds. To think that God Himself cares enough about us to speak directly to us in this special way should always give us a sense of awe. We forget what the Bible really is sometimes and therefore we do not realize when we study it how privileged we are to be able to understand it. Through the Bible, we can understand God Himself and His plan for the ages. We can also allow it to change us and make us into a person of outstanding courage and character.

Copy all of Hebrews 4:12 here. _____

_____

_____

_____

List some of the special powers the Word of God claims in this verse.

- _____

- _____

- _____

Life Principle: The Word of God should change us.

God Speaks To Moses

One of the best examples of God's speaking directly to someone in the Bible is in the story of Moses. God had specifically chosen Moses to lead the nation of Israel out of Egypt and out of slavery. Moses was an old man—eighty years old—when God spoke to him. God had been preparing Moses for this task for many years. But now, when the time God had chosen had arrived, Moses was not sure he was ready. He began to make excuses to God.

Look up each of the following verses in the Book of Exodus. In your own words, explain Moses' excuses and how God responded to him.

Verses	Moses' Excuse	God's Response
3:11–12		
3:13–14		
4:1–4		
4:10–12		

In these passages, we can see the certainty of God's promises through His Word. God knows that if we are willing, He can give us power to do anything He wants for us. Look at the chart again and notice the promises God made to Moses.

Moses made many excuses to God, but he never told God he was unwilling. If he had not been willing, God might have chosen someone else. But God knew Moses' heart and met his need. When Moses stopped giving excuses, God used him in a great way.

From your past studies, what do you remember about God's purpose for Moses in His plan?

_____

_____

 What does the Bible say about Moses in Deuteronomy 34:10–12?

_____

_____

_____

Simon The Zealot

Jesus had two disciples named Simon. Jesus changed the name of one of them to Peter, and most Christians are very familiar with the type of man Simon Peter was. Though he denied Christ before He died, this man became a great preacher after Christ's resurrection.

The other Simon is not well known. In fact, he is only mentioned a couple of times. In Luke 6:15 he is called "the Zealot" or "Zelotes." This was a nickname. It referred to a political group of those times called the Zealots.

 Look up the words "zeal," "zealot," and "zealous" in the dictionary and use the meanings to explain the type of man Simon probably was.

_____

_____

_____

At the time of Christ, the Roman Empire was very strong. The Romans had control of Israel, and all the Jews were under the power of their government. The Zealots were a band of Jewish men who wanted Israel to have her freedom. They wanted to overthrow the Roman government.

Simon was a member of the Zealots who felt they could take on the whole Roman army. Their lives were "on fire for a cause." They were devoted to Israel. When Simon became a believer, Jesus changed his zeal away from politics. Jesus was a zealot—but not a Zealot. We read that He had a zeal for His Father's house when He cleansed the temple. Like Jesus, Simon was now "on fire" for spiritual things.

This is the way God wants us to live. Sometimes Christians have a "don't care" attitude, and then nothing satisfies them. When a Christian is full of fire and zeal, life is very full and exciting.

As we study the Word of God this year, God wants you to become zealous for spirtual things and zealous to learn more about Him.

Winning Your Race

Read Revelation 3:15–16. What kind of Christian are you? Are you hot or cold, or are you lukewarm?

What kind of attitude does God want Christians to have? _____
_____

Read 1 Chronicles 28:9 and, in your own words, tell what kind of heart and mind God is looking for. _____
_____
_____

Imagine that God was talking directly to you as He talked to Moses. Think through all of the verses we have studied in this lesson. What would God say to you about the attitude of your heart and mind? _____
_____
_____
_____

Unit Two:
Developing Inner Strength

Key Verse: 1 John 2:14

Athletes who compete in the Olympic games, particularly those who compete in the decathlon, must develop their inner strength to become the best athlete in their particular competition. Many, many times it is that one athlete who has an extra measure of inner strength who becomes the winner.

Athletes don't just compete against one another. They also must be attentive to time and distance standards. The competition is really a test of the athlete's speed, agility, endurance, and strength.

Christians are not called to compete against one another at all. We are competing against the strengths and weaknesses within ourselves. It is our inner weaknesses of character that will cause us to fail and not achieve our full potential. God wants to develop our inner character and strength so that we might be strong in the world and have an honorable and victorious life.

We must learn, therefore, that God has a purpose for us, that He wants to fill us with His Holy Spirit to give us His strength, and that our inner strength of character must come from God Himself. These are the lessons we will learn in Unit Two.

God's Design For Me

Key Verse: Psalm 98:1

VOCABULARY

Warrior: a fighting man; soldier

Midianites: a tribe that descended from a son of Abraham. They were nomads, but in the time of Moses they had great wealth.

Valor: personal strength and courage

Smite: to strike heavily or to kill someone with a heavy blow

I Am Important To God

One of the most important things God wants us to learn from His Word is that He has a specific purpose for our lives. Since God is good, we can know that He intends to accomplish something good through the way He has made us and the work He has given us to do.

God took great care when He created us. He wants us to realize that He made us just the way He did so that we would be able to make other people think great things about God and believe in Him. Even our weaknesses or deficiencies provide opportunities for others to see God work in our lives. God knows that it is important for us to learn to be happy and content with the way He made you. If you are thankful for the way He made you, you will enjoy your friends, your work, and your family. In fact, you will enjoy all of life more. You will also enjoy your God more!

Most of us, however, usually wish we were different in some way. Name some things right now that you have wished were different about yourself.

_____

_____

_____

Usually, when we think this way, it is because we do not realize that God designed us in a special way. We believe that we could have done a better job than the Creator of the universe.

✎ Read Romans 9:20–21. What does God tell us about these kinds of thoughts?

_____

_____

_____

_____

Now read Psalm 100. These verses also tell us that it is God who made us. Note that the attitude of the person who wrote this psalm is completely different from the man who believes he knows better than God how he should have been made.

✎ List at least three things from this psalm that God would like to see in your attitudes.

• _____

• _____

• _____

These verses teach us that if we are happy in our hearts for the way God designed us, we will be happy with all of life. We will be able to trust God more easily.

Life Principle: God designed me in a unique and special way for a specific purpose.

God Made Me For A Purpose

God has definitely designed you in a special way, and He makes no mistakes. He designed how you look, what you are good at doing, what you are not good at doing, your personality, your family—in fact, all of you!

✎ Describe God's design for you in the following areas:

• Appearance: _____

_____

_____

• Abilities: _____

_____

_____

• Parents and family: _____

_____

_____

• Personality: _____

_____

_____

✎ List some talents or abilities that God planned for you not to have.

_____
_____
_____

Before you can really understand more of God's plan for your life, you must learn to see yourself from God's point of view. Looking at yourself from God's viewpoint is simply being able to thank Him for designing you exactly as you are.

✎ If you wish you could change something about yourself, are you really being thankful to God?
_____

Learning To Trust God

You can always trust God to make the right decisions. Because of His love for you, you can know that He designed you without mistake. Look up the following verses. What does each verse say that can help you understand His love for you?

✎ Psalm 18:30: _____
_____

✎ Psalm 139:17–18: _____
_____

✎ Jeremiah 29:11: _____
_____

✎ John 10:10: _____
_____

The Story Of Gideon

Gideon was designed by God for a great purpose, but he almost missed out on finding God's purpose because of his attitude toward himself.

The Israelites had rebelled against the Lord. Because of this, God allowed the Midianites to conquer them and leave them in poverty. The Israelites now begged the Lord to help them. Therefore, God heard their cries and sent an angel to search out Gideon.

Read Judges 6:11–17. As you answer the following questions, think how important it is to think highly of the way God made you.

- What was the angel's first remark to Gideon (vs. 12)? _____
  _____

- What was Gideon's attitude toward God (vs. 13)? _____
  _____
  _____

- What did the angel say God's plan for Gideon was to be (vs. 14)? _____
  _____

- How did Gideon see himself (vs. 15)? _____
  _____
  _____

- What was the Lord's attitude toward Gideon (vs. 16)? _____
  _____
  _____

Based on what we have studied in this lesson, explain what was wrong with Gideon's thoughts about himself. _____
_____
_____
_____

If you could have talked to Gideon, what would you have told him so he could have gained a better attitude about what God could do through him? _____
_____
_____
_____

Praising God For His Design

Being happy and proud of the way we are made does not mean we are big-headed or conceited. We are praising God for His work.

Copy Psalm 139:14 below and make it a personal message to God.

_____
_____
_____

Can you now understand that God planned you without a mistake? Can you now be thankful for every part of your design? Reread Psalm 100:3. Bow your head and really give thanks to God for the way He made you.

Read the story of Gideon in Judges 6, 7, and 8. Imagine that you were there when these events occurred, and answer the following questions.

How do you think Gideon felt when he was destroying his father's idols?

_____

_____

Do you think Gideon needed the sign of the fleece in order to know what God really wanted him to do? _____ Why or why not? _____

_____

What do you think Gideon's 300 soldiers thought about going to face the Midianites with such a small force?

_____

_____

_____

Why do you think God planned to send such a small force into battle?

_____

_____

_____

How would you have felt about going into battle with only a trumpet, a torch, and a pitcher?

_____

_____

_____

Who was responsible for Israel's victory? _____

Why do you think Gideon refused to become the ruler of Israel?

_____

_____

LESSON 5
God's Purpose For Me

Key Verse: John 16:33

Our last lesson pointed out that God took very great care to design us. We are all so different—our abilities are different, our families and homes are so varied, and of course, our looks are so very different too. We need to be thankful continually that God made us as we are.

But this is just a part of God's plan for your life. He designed you with a purpose in mind. He is continually working to fulfill His purpose for your life.

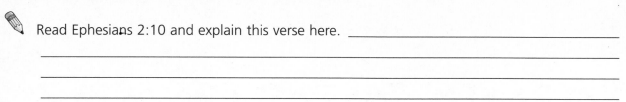 Read Ephesians 2:10 and explain this verse here. _____

_____

_____

_____

When we say that God is working to fulfill His purposes through our lives, we simply mean that He had a plan for you before you were born, and it is His goal to complete that plan and purpose.

My Ultimate Purpose

As you read the following verses, find the overall purpose that God has for your life. For each verse, explain one aspect of God's purpose for you.

Isaiah 43:7: _____

Romans 9:17: _____

_____

Philippians 1:6: _____

_____

A Time For Every Activity Under Heaven

This truth is from Ecclesiastes 3:1. In this passage, God explains that each day has a definite purpose—a definite job for each of us. Explain what a few of God's purposes for your life are right now—at home, at school, at church, and in other places. How can you show His power and bring glory to God in each of these areas?

	God's Purpose For Me	How This Can Bring Glory To God And Show His Power
Home		
School		
Church		
Other		

How Does God Work Out His Purpose For Me?

In order to fulfill God's purpose for your life, God has given you many people to help you plan and guide your life. Name some of these people. But each of these people can only help you externally. They can never get inside you to help you change internally. Only God can do that!

Look up these two words and explain their meanings below in your own words.

• Internal: _____

• External: _____

What does 1 Samuel 16:7 say that relates to these two words? _____

_____

_____

Your external design is basically finished. It cannot be changed very much. But God wants to continue to work internally on your character through your entire life.

 Read Romans 8:28–29. God says that He works in all things for the good of those who love Him, to those who have been called according to His purpose so that they might be conformed

_____

He made you perfect (exactly as He wanted you to be) externally, and now He wants to perfect (or complete) you internally.

Life Principle: God's purpose is to conform you to the image of Jesus Christ.

For this to happen, Jesus Christ must be living inside you. You must make sure you have trusted Jesus Christ as your Lord and Savior. This is most important for several reasons.

 First, you cannot go to heaven and have eternal life until Jesus Christ becomes your Savior. Why is this so (Rom. 3:23)? _____

_____

 Second, there is only one way to have our sin taken away. How can this take place (Rom. 5:8–9)? _____

_____

_____

 Third, there is only one way to know for sure that Christ has indeed become your Savior. Do you know for sure that you will be in heaven one day? How do you know (1 John 5:12–13)?

_____

_____

Winning Your Race

In your own words, explain how a person becomes a believer.

_____

_____

_____

_____

_____

Again, in your own words, explain the following phrases:

• God fulfills His purpose in you.

_____

_____

_____

• Inner character

_____

_____

_____

• Conformed to the likeness of His Son

_____

_____

_____

Your life is important to God, but the biggest question is whether you will allow God to fulfill His purpose in you. Will you yield to God as He intends to teach you the things that will make you strong in character?

How can you know that these things are true? Because of what Jesus Christ did on the cross for you! The cross tells you how important you are to God—it expresses the love of God for you.

Read 1 John 4. Find and write out three verses that show God's love for you.

_____

_____

_____

_____

_____

_____

_____

_____

LESSON 6
Being Filled With The Spirit

Key Verse: Ephesians 5:18

VOCABULARY

Conviction: being strongly convinced of something. When we are convicted of sin, we are strongly convinced by the Holy Spirit that we are wrong and need to repent.

Filled with the Spirit: being controlled by the Spirit of God within us. This means that we are allowing the Holy Spirit to direct, regulate, restrain, and influence our lives.

In our last lesson, we learned that God has a purpose for our lives. Part of this purpose involves day by day goals that God has for us to accomplish. He also has a primary goal of building our inner character so that we are conformed to the likeness of His Son. But our main purpose in life will always be:

- To bring glory to the Lord in all we do.
- To show God's power through our lives.

In this lesson we are going to learn more about the Holy Spirit and His work in you.

God Gives Us A Command

If you have trusted Jesus Christ as your Savior, the Holy Spirit has come to live in you. When you feel guilty about a sin, it is the Holy Spirit living within you who makes you know you were wrong. The Holy Spirit wants you to confess the sin to God. The Holy Spirit is the one who accomplishes God's work in your heart and mind so that you desire to do God's will. Read Ephesians 5:18–21 to learn how the Holy Spirit works.

 God gives you a command in Ephesians 5:18. What does He tell you to do?

_____

Life Principle: Being "filled with the Spirit" means to be controlled completely by Him.

Being "filled with the Spirit" means you are letting the Holy Spirit use your mind, hands, feet...all of you to bring glory to God. When you do wrong, the Holy Spirit is not in control. You must then confess your sin to God and allow the Spirit to be in control again.

Evidences Of Being Filled With The Spirit

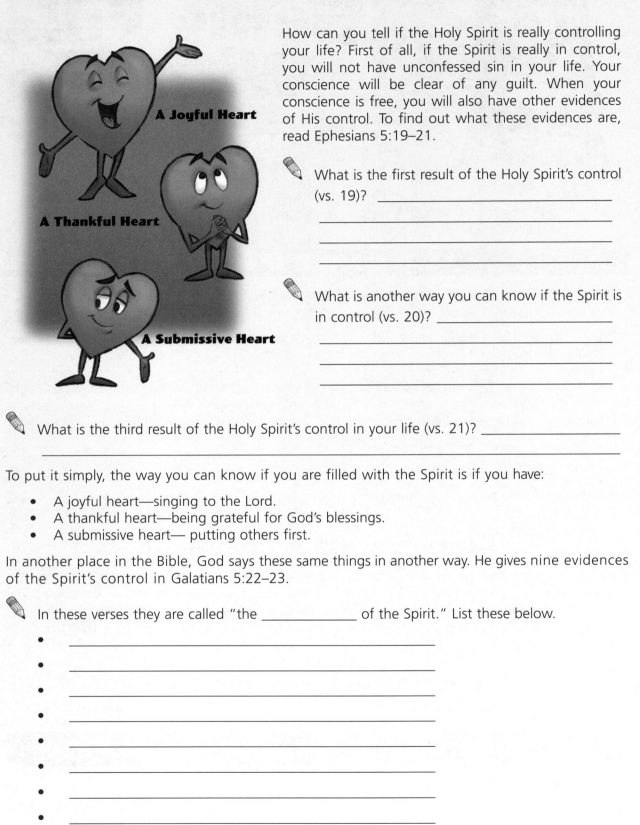

A Joyful Heart

A Thankful Heart

A Submissive Heart

How can you tell if the Holy Spirit is really controlling your life? First of all, if the Spirit is really in control, you will not have unconfessed sin in your life. Your conscience will be clear of any guilt. When your conscience is free, you will also have other evidences of His control. To find out what these evidences are, read Ephesians 5:19–21.

What is the first result of the Holy Spirit's control (vs. 19)? _____
_____
_____
_____

What is another way you can know if the Spirit is in control (vs. 20)? _____
_____
_____
_____

What is the third result of the Holy Spirit's control in your life (vs. 21)? _____
_____

To put it simply, the way you can know if you are filled with the Spirit is if you have:

- A joyful heart—singing to the Lord.
- A thankful heart—being grateful for God's blessings.
- A submissive heart— putting others first.

In another place in the Bible, God says these same things in another way. He gives nine evidences of the Spirit's control in Galatians 5:22–23.

In these verses they are called "the _____ of the Spirit." List these below.

- _____
- _____
- _____
- _____
- _____
- _____
- _____
- _____
- _____

Attributes Of Self-Control

What do these verses teach about how we demonstrate self-control?

Proverbs 16:32: _____
_____

Proverbs 21:23: _____
_____

Romans 6:12: _____
_____

Galatians 5:22–23: _____
_____

Hebrews 13:17: _____
_____

James 3:2: _____
_____

2 Peter 1:6: _____
_____

An Example Of The Spirit-Filled Life

Read Acts 16:22–31. Here is a story that shows the results of being filled with the Spirit. In the story, God had been using Paul and Silas to preach about Jesus Christ. This angered many of the authorities, and they decided to stop them.

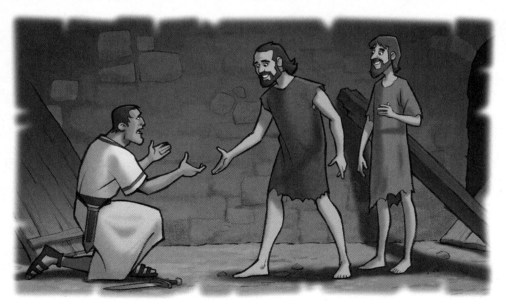

If Paul and Silas had to depend on external circumstances, would they have been happy? What had happened to them (vv. 22–24)? _____

_____

Based on what we have learned, how do you know that Paul and Silas were filled with the Spirit (vs. 25)? _____

_____

Because they were joyful and thankful and submissive to their captors, how was God able to use them (vv. 26–31)? _____

_____

_____

Winning Your Race

In your own words, explain what you believe is the secret of continual joy and happiness.

_____

_____

_____

_____

_____

If you are truly controlled by the Spirit of God, what will your attitude be...

- When your mother reminds you to clean your room? _____

  _____

- When you have lots of homework to finish? _____

  _____

- When you don't get the clothes or toy you have been wanting? _____

  _____

- When someone tells a lie about you? _____

  _____

- When your parents ask you to do something, but you want to continue to play?

  _____

- When your little brother or sister scribbles on your work? _____

  _____

- When the dog next door rips up your baseball glove? _____

  _____

- When your brother or sister gets into your things without asking? _____

  _____

- When you are asked to do something over because it was not done right the first time?

  _____

Key Verses: Luke 1:46–47

VOCABULARY

Honor: to hold in high esteem

Glorify: to cause to appear magnificent to others by presenting in a favorable aspect

Praise: to express great approval of something or someone; to commend highly

Everyone wants to be happy. Most young people feel they would be happy if they could be the prettiest or most popular person in school or could get straight A's or be the best player on the baseball team. But this is not how you become happy. As soon as you get what you want, you will desire something else. Happiness or joy does not come from the things this world offers.

Life Principle: True happiness depends on who we worship and love the most and what we are on the inside, not on what we have on the outside.

Jesus Christ was the poorest of the poor, yet He was supremely happy even though He was going to die on the cross.

Mary: A Joyful Woman

In this lesson we are going to learn more about a young woman who had very few possessions but was truly happy. This young woman's name was Mary, and she was the mother of Jesus. Let's find out what made Mary happy and how you can be happy too.

 First of all, Mary was happy because she trusted God as her Savior. Read Luke 1:47 and tell how Mary felt about this fact. _____

_____

Salvation is the first step to being truly happy. No one can have real joy and peace unless he first has Christ living inside him.

The second reason Mary was happy was that she allowed the Holy Spirit to control her life. Read Luke 1:35. What great blessing was the power of God going to give Mary?

_____
_____
_____

When the Holy Spirit has power over or control of your life, what can you expect (Luke 1:49)? _____
_____
_____
_____

Finally, Mary was happy because she knew her purpose in life was to bring glory to God by praising Him continually. Read Luke 1:46 and 49 and explain the reasons Mary's soul gave thanks to the Lord. _____
_____

Look up the word "glorify." What does it mean? _____
_____
_____

Look again at verses 46 and 47. Mary glorified God in her soul and rejoiced in her spirit. Does this mean that her joy came from within or from outside circumstances? _____ Was her joy dependent on something internal or external? _____

Glorifying And Praising God

We have already seen that the word "glorify" means to make something or someone seem great or important.

Now look up the following similar words and write their definitions:

- Honor: _____

- Praise: _____
    _____

The Bible teaches that our main purpose in life is to bring glory to God. Just as Mary did, we glorify God by praising Him for everything that happens to us! This is the attitude that brings joy inside us.

Each of the following verses emphasizes God's purpose in us. Remember: Our purpose is to bring praise and glory to the Lord, and He will provide our joy.

Tell how each of these verses explains this idea.

- Ephesians 1:6: _____
  _____

- Ephesians 1:12: _____
  _____

- Ephesians 5:20: _____
  _____

- Philippians 4:4: _____
  _____

- Hebrews 13:15: _____
  _____

Winning Your Race

What is God's purpose for your life?
_____
_____

How can you bring glory to God by
your life? _____
_____
_____
_____
_____

What should be your attitude when
something seems to go wrong?
_____
_____
_____
_____
_____

Based on the verses we just studied, does God ever want you to complain or grumble? _____

Comparing her life to ours, the mother of Jesus should have been very unhappy. She lived in a tiny village that was not well respected. She was very poor. She didn't have the things we take for granted. But she was happy because of what she had in her heart.

We talked about the three things that caused Mary to be happy. List them below.

1. _____

_____

2. _____

_____

3. _____

_____

Be honest! Which of the above is a part of your life now? _____

_____

Which ones are you going to have to learn more about and put into practice?

_____

_____

Key Verse: 1 John 1:9

VOCABULARY

Rage or wrath: violent anger

Brawling or clamour: noisy shouting; vigorous protesting or demanding

Anger: a strong feeling of displeasure

Bitterness: intense or severe distress or hatred

Confession: an acknowledgment of guilt

Grieve: to cause heavy sadness or sorrow

Unrighteousness: sinfulness; wickedness; injustice

Slander or evil speaking: saying hurtful or negative things about others

As we have already learned, God has a purpose for your life. His goals for you are always the highest and finest possible. Many people fail to yield to these goals and fulfill God's purpose for their lives. The reason they fail is because they rebel against God's commands.

Life Principle: You need to learn to confess your sins and let God cleanse them from your life.

After you confess your sins to the Lord, trust Him to give you the wisdom and courage to go on to reach His goals for your life.

Grieving The Holy Spirit

There are many ways we can fall into sin and fail in some area of our lives. Ephesians 4:30–32 discusses some of the most common problems we face. Read these verses.

As you read, you will find the following terms. Look up each word and write the definitions.

- Bitterness: _____

- Rage or wrath: _____

- Anger: _____

- Brawling or clamour: _____
  _____

- Slander or evil speaking: _____
  _____

What does verse 30 say these things do to the Holy Spirit? _____
_____

What does this mean? _____

Can you be filled (controlled) by the Spirit when you are doing these things? _____

What To Do When You Sin

When you do sin, God has a definite way to help you. Read 1 John 1:9. From this verse, explain what God says you must do when you sin. _____

To "confess" a sin to God is to admit to God that you have sinned against Him and to agree with His attitude toward that sin.

After you have done your part by admitting to God that you were wrong, God promises to do two things. What are they?

- _____

- _____

Failure Turned Into Victory

One of the writers of the Gospels was a man named John Mark. The Bible indicates Mark had family members who were believers. Barnabas and Paul encouraged him in his faith and his ministry, and Peter probably had a close relationship to him as well. Soon after he was saved, the Apostle Paul and Barnabas were called by God to become the first missionaries of the church.

 Read how God chose them in Acts 13:2–5. Who told them to do this work and then sent them forth? ____

_____

According to verse 5, who went along to help them and minister to their needs so they could preach the gospel? _____ (Note: This was John Mark.) These three men traveled together for some weeks, but something was wrong.

What did John Mark do in Acts 13:13? _____

_____

The Bible does not tell us why John Mark left Paul, but Paul did not appreciate his departure. We know that Mark had done wrong because of what happened in Acts 15:36–40. Paul and Barnabas were going to travel together again.

Whom did Barnabas wish to take with them? _____

Why did Paul refuse to take him? _____

_____

_____

Because they disagreed, what finally happened between Paul and Barnabas? _____

_____

_____

Because Mark had done wrong, Paul did not trust him, but Barnabas wanted to help Mark grow into a man of God. Mark could have given up because of Paul's attitude toward him, but he admitted he had done wrong and let the Lord rule his life. God began to work in Mark's life, and He used Mark's life in a great way.

God even gave him the privilege of writing the Gospel of _____.

We know that Mark learned to be a dependable man of God because years later we find that Paul had changed his mind. In 2 Timothy 4:11, Paul asked Timothy to _____ _____ because _____

_____ .

Learning From Past Failures

From the story of Mark, we can learn many lessons. Review these lessons by looking up the following verses:

First of all, we need to remember the truth of Romans 3:23, which says that all _____

_____

Secondly, because he was a sinner like everyone else, John Mark had to do what Jesus Christ said in John 3:7. What was it? _____

This happens when we trust Christ as our Lord and Savior and are born into God's family.

The third lesson we must learn is that there will be times when we do wrong just as Mark did. How does 1 John 1:9 remind us what must be done when you do something wrong?

_____

_____

_____

Another lesson we must learn is that even when we fail, God is ready to make things right again. What is the promise of God in Psalm 37:24? _____

_____

_____

The last lesson we can learn is seen in Paul's life because he changed his attitude toward Mark. This attitude is discussed in the verses we have already considered. What attitude does God want us to learn according to Ephesians 4:32? _____

_____

_____

So, the five lessons we can learn from the story of Mark are:

- All of us are sinners.
- Because we are sinners, we need to be born again.
- Even after we are saved, we still sin.
- When we sin, God is ready to make things right again if we confess our sins to Him.
- We should be ready to forgive the sins of others too.

Winning Your Race

Have you been born again?

_____

_____

Is there something that you have done that needs to be confessed to God? Explain.

_____

_____

Remember: If you confess the sin and turn from it, the Lord will help you not to do the same thing again. You will never be perfect, but you will be growing.

Is there someone you need to forgive? Explain.

_____

_____

Unit Three:
Striving For The Prize

The youngest person ever to win the decathlon event was Bob Mathias. The world focused great attention on this event in 1948 because the winner of the gold medal was so young. Bob Mathias was only seventeen years old when he won this most prestigious of all athletic events. Bob Mathias' victory showed the world that a young man with determination to train and great strength of character could achieve great honor in life.

God does not judge us by our ages. He perceives our maturity and strength as Christians. To achieve the best that God has for us, we must develop in certain important areas of our lives. We must first determine to place God at the center of our lives and allow Him to teach us how to obey Him. We must continually honor those who have authority over us, especially to honor and obey our parents. We must realize that our inner character is much more important than our outward reputation because sooner or later, what we are inside will be evident to all. Above all, we must learn to have the courage to stand for what is true and right at all costs and not allow rebellion or pride to stand in our way. We must learn not to allow friends or wrong activities to draw us away from the high goals God has called us to achieve in our lives. This unit of study will help you to see the importance of these things for your own life.

Just as Bob Mathias as a young man had the courage to set a great goal for himself and to commit himself to accomplish that goal, so can you achieve your goals if you have the courage to stand for what is right.

Key Verse: Ephesians 5:17

Making Wrong Choices

The story of Lot is one of the most interesting in the Bible. Lot joined Abraham in leaving their homeland for a land that God would show them. For a time, Lot did enjoy God's blessing on his life, but then he put his own desires and will ahead of God and eventually lost everything. Fill in the blanks below from the Bible references, and you will see why Lot's life ended in failure. All of the verses are from the book of Genesis.

 God called _____ (13:1) and Lot out of the land of _____. Abram and Lot were both very wealthy because God had greatly blessed their lives. Abram had an _____ (13:4) made to the Lord and prayed there, but Lot had given up his altar. Soon there was _____ (13:7) between Abram's and Lot's _____. Abram told Lot to _____ (13:9) and choose what _____ he wished. Lot chose the best land, which was _____ (13:10). Abram lived in _____ (13:12), and Lot's land was near _____. The men in that city were _____ (13:13).

Abram had the right spirit because he let Lot choose first. Lot did not consider other people or what choice would honor God. He just chose the land that looked the best. God knew that land would be destroyed. Lot had placed his own will before God's.

 The cities of Sodom and Gomorrah were very wicked, and God was going to destroy them. Abram (now called Abraham) went before God in prayer and begged Him to _____ (18:24) the city if he could find fifty _____ people. The Lord even said He would spare the city if Abraham could find _____ (18:32) such people. But the city was far too wicked.

At first, Lot set his heart toward Sodom, but finally he was living within the _____ (19:1) of Sodom. He became a part of that wicked city and was ashamed to let anyone know that he believed in God. Lot wanted to get his own way rather than follow God. Lot probably thought he was wiser than Abraham because he appeared to be more successful. Then the Lord sent two _____ (19:1) to Lot. The angels told Lot to _____ _____ (19:12–13) because God would destroy the city. Lot, his wife, and his two daughters finally fled, and God rained _____ upon the wicked cities (19:24). Lot's wife looked back, and she became _____ (19:26). Because Lot was so far out of God's will, he and his daughters ended up dwelling in a _____ (19:30).

In your own words, explain why a rich and successful man such as Lot ended up penniless and living in a cave. _____
_____
_____
_____

Steps Away From God

Failure does not happen all at once. When you disobey God and do not confess your sins to God, it is easier to sin again. Lot took the first step of disobedience to God and did not confess his sin to the Lord. That made it easier and easier to sin again and again. Soon, Lot had become a failure. List the steps to Lot's failure below.

Genesis	Steps In Lot's Failure
13:10–11	
13:12–13	
19:1	
19:30	

Remember, the world, like Sodom and Gomorrah, will pass away, but the man _____
_____ (1 John 2:17). This
is God's promise to us.

Anything that causes us to disobey God's will is of the world. Things of the world may look good and appear good; however, if they come before God, they are sin. God wants us always to choose Him before all else. Good character is found in the choices we make.

In our last lesson, we learned about John Mark. He also made a wrong decision, but later God was able to greatly bless his life. Lot's life ended in failure.

What was the difference between Mark and Lot? _____
_____
_____
_____

When you fail, what should you do as soon as you know you have done wrong?
_____

Choosing God's Way

Lot's biggest mistake was in putting his own will ahead of God's. God could not bless his life because of this. In fact, because Lot set his heart and will against God and toward evil, he ended up losing everything he had. This should be a very important lesson for us.

> **Life Principle:** As a Christian, you must continually decide whether you will choose God's way or your own way. Choosing God's way is yielding your will to God and then obeying His Word.

This principle is so important to God that He says it over and over again. In your own words, tell what each of the following verses says about doing God's will:

Proverbs 3:6: _____
_____

Ephesians 5:17: _____
_____

Philippians 2:13: _____
_____

Hebrews 10:36: _____
_____

Hebrews 13:21: _____
_____

Winning Your Race

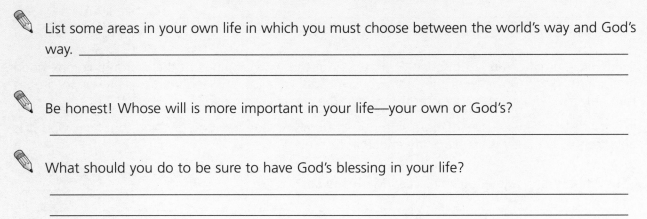 List some areas in your own life in which you must choose between the world's way and God's way. _____

_____

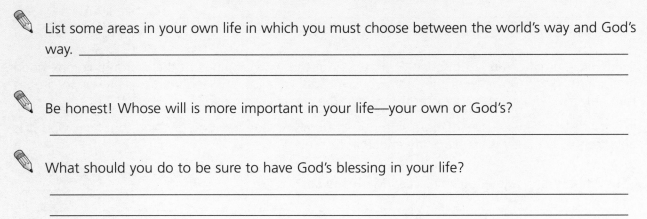 Be honest! Whose will is more important in your life—your own or God's?

_____

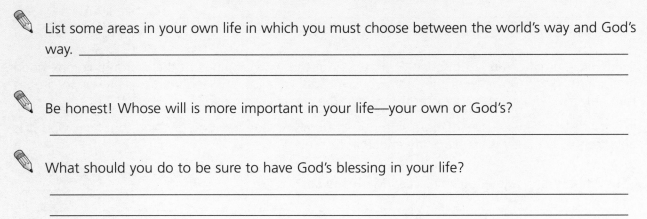 What should you do to be sure to have God's blessing in your life?

_____

_____

Key Verse: Ephesians 6:1

VOCABULARY

Rebellion: resistance or defiance of established authority

In lessons ten and eleven, we are going to study the lives of two sons of wealthy fathers. The first, Isaac, honored and respected his father, and God gave him a life of blessing and success. The second son we will study is Absalom, a son of King David. Absalom's life shows what happens to someone who rebels against authority and wastes his life.

Life Principle: One of the most important aspects of being in God's will is honoring and obeying our parents.

Commands And Promises

We have just finished studying a story about Abraham and Lot. We have seen what happened because of disobedience in Lot's life. Abraham's life was very different. Abraham was rich materially, but he was even richer spiritually because he always put God first. God chose Abraham and his family to give the Bible and the Savior to the world. In this lesson we are going to study about Abraham and his son Isaac. Isaac would often hear Abraham talking about God's promises to His children.

 Read 1 John 5:2. What does God say will be true of you if you are born into His family?

_____

Throughout the Bible, God gives us commands to obey. He never gives a command without a special blessing for those who obey. To see this for yourself, turn to Proverbs 3 and find some of the commands and blessings in verses 1–10.

Command	Blessing
3:1	3:2
3:3	3:4
3:5–6	3:6
3:7	3:8
3:9	3:10

Remember: When God gives us a command, there is also a blessing that is ours if we will obey His command. These promises of God are encouragements for us to desire to do His will always.

The First Commandment With A Promise

God told Abraham's son, and He also tells you, that the first and most important command is that we honor and obey our parents.

 Read Ephesians 6:1–3 and write the commandment found in those verses. _____

_____

 What does God promise you in these same verses if you obey? _____

_____

Perhaps you know of a young person who became very sick or who was involved in a serious accident and did not survive. Does this mean that this young person did not honor his or her parents or that God didn't keep His promise? Certainly not! Instead, we can know for certain that the blessings this young person will receive in heaven for obedience will far surpass a long and happy life on earth.

Isaac kept God's commands in this area, and God was able to greatly bless his life, as you will learn.

Abraham's Toughest Test

We are going to study a very strange story. Turn to Genesis 22. As you study the story, remember that sometimes in your own life, God will want you to do things that you do not understand. He always has a good reason, and He will always bless your life if you obey!

✏ What did God tell Abraham to do (vv. 1–2)? _____

_____

✏ What was Abraham's immediate response (vs. 3)? _____

_____

✏ Do you think Abraham wanted to kill his son? _____

✏ What does Abraham's attitude tell you about his faith in God? _____

_____

_____

_____

✏ What did Abraham do to Isaac when they reached the appointed place (vv. 9–10)?

_____

_____

_____

✏ Abraham was very old, and Isaac was young and strong. Isaac could have pushed his father away and run very easily. Since he did not do this, what does this tell you about Isaac? ____

_____

_____

✏ What did God do at the last moment (vv. 11–13)? _____

_____

✏ God did not want Isaac to die, but He did have a purpose in this. God wanted Isaac's and Abraham's hearts completely surrendered and yielded to do His will. How do you know that God truly had their hearts? _____

_____

Blessed Are The Meek

One of the character traits Isaac possessed that helped him to be obedient to his father was meekness. Meekness is the attitude that accepts God's working in our lives, whether it understands His purpose or not.

What do these verses teach about how God treats those who are meek and humble?

Psalm 25:9: _____

Psalm 37:11: _____

Psalm 149:4: _____

Isaiah 29:19: _____

Matthew 5:5: _____

Winning Your Race

Can you imagine what trust it took for Isaac to go with his father and then to allow Abraham to lay him on the altar? He didn't ask a lot of questions but obeyed willingly. And can you imagine how Abraham felt about what he was doing? Yet he obeyed and trusted God to make the right decision for his life.

This is the way to the blessing of God in your life too. Think now about your own attitude at home. Be honest in answering the following questions:

What is your usual attitude when your parents ask you to do something?

_____

_____

How well do you accept the responsibility for your routine chores?

_____

_____

How do you accept criticism when your parents must teach you when you're wrong?

_____

_____

Do you ever try to show your parents your love by doing something without being told? Give an example. _____

_____

Do you go to your parents for advice? Give an example.

_____

_____

How can you help make your home happy and pleasant?

_____

_____

When did you last tell your parents that you loved them?

_____

_____

Now look back over your answers. Are you really giving honor and respect to your parents as God asks?_____ Is God able to bless your life as He wants to? _____

Key Verse: 1 Samuel 16:7

VOCABULARY

Pride: an excessively high opinion of oneself

Deceive: to lead a person to believe something that is not true; to mislead

Haughty: proud and vain to the point of being arrogant

Reputation: how a person is generally perceived by others

Character: a person's moral nature; the combination of qualities that make one person different from another

Ambition: a strong desire to get or become something

In this lesson we are going to study about a man who was completely opposed to God's command to honor his parents. His name was Absalom. Find out who Absalom was in 2 Samuel 3:2–3.

_____

_____

Describe Absalom from 2 Samuel 14:25–28. Include what these verses say about his attitude toward his father. _____

_____

_____

_____

_____

_____

Absalom was a very handsome man, the son of a king who had no trouble making friends because everyone praised him. Absalom should have been able to have a happy and joyful life with all that God had given him. But he had a great weakness—the wrong heart attitude. The kind of heart attitude you have—your true inner character—determines the kind of life you will lead. Absalom's "heart problem" ruined his life.

A Rebellious Son

Absalom was a rebellious son because he tried to take over his father's kingdom. Begin reading 2 Samuel 15 and answer the following questions to see how Absalom worked out his deceitful ambition. He wanted the kingdom for himself.

✎ What was Absalom's purpose in the beginning (vv. 4–6)? _____

_____

✎ What religious lie did Absalom tell his father, King David (vs. 7)? _____

_____

✎ Where did he go, and what was his plan of deceit (vv. 9–10)? _____

_____

_____

✎ What did David find that his son had done (vv. 12–13)? _____

_____

_____

✎ What did King David do then (vs. 14)? _____

_____

✎ In what ways had Absalom broken God's commandment to honor his father and mother?

_____

_____

_____

Good Reputation Or Good Character?

Absalom was a rebellious son because he tried to take over his father's kingdom. The following words describe some of Absalom's sin problems.

✎ Write their meanings to make sure you understand what was wrong in Absalom's heart.

- Rebellion: _____

  _____

- Pride: _____

  _____

- Deceit: _____

  _____

- Reputation: _____

  _____

- Character: _____
  _____
  _____

- Ambition: _____
  _____

Do you remember when we studied the difference between our external characteristics and our internal character? Basically, reputation refers to what others see of us on the outside. It is external. Our character is what we really are on the inside. We can hide poor character for a while, but soon our character will affect our reputation.

> **Life Principle:** We can look good to others on the outside, but if our internal character is not right, it will soon be evident to others.

Absalom's inner character of pride, rebellion, and deceit finally led to his downfall. At first, others only saw a handsome man who seemed to be a great leader. But Absalom's purposes were wrong within his heart, so he eventually had to fail. God could not bless his life.

The Results Of Pride And Rebellion

Absalom had started his rebellion in Hebron and had gained many followers. Now he was so popular that he was welcomed in Jerusalem where the king himself lived. He told the people, "My father isn't taking care of you properly," and he stole the people's hearts. Absalom's reputation was excellent.

Absalom had built an army, and now he led his army against his own father. How great his pride was now! He had rejected both his father and the Lord. God would not bless him now.

Before you learn what happened to Absalom, notice his father's attitude toward his son even after his rebellion.

What did David command his men to do (2 Sam. 18:5)? _____
_____

Describe the battle that took place because of Absalom's rebellious heart (2 Sam. 18:7–8).
_____
_____

What was the final outcome of Absalom's life (2 Sam. 18:9–15)? _____
_____
_____

How did David feel when he learned of his son's death (2 Sam. 18:32–33)? _____
_____
_____

The Results Of Humility

Now that we have seen the results of pride and rebellion in the life of Absalom, let's see what the Bible has to say about the opposite of pride—humility. What do these verses teach about how God treats those who are meek and humble?

Proverbs 15:33: _____

Proverbs 22:4: _____

_____

Proverbs 29:23: _____

_____

Luke 14:11: _____

_____

1 Peter 5:5: _____

Winning Your Race

You can never understand how very much your parents love you. When you are proud, rebellious, or disrespectful, it hurts them very much. But they still love you and want your life to be right.

Absalom's life looked successful to his followers because he had a good reputation. But in the eyes of God, he had to fail. This was because his inner character was wrong, and he had failed to keep the first commandment with a promise.

What was this commandment? _____

Notice again the definitions of "reputation" and "character." Which is more important to God?

_____

Which will God bless? _____

Which will therefore bring you a joyful, successful life? _____

LESSON 12
God Wants Your Heart

Key Verse: Proverbs 23:26

VOCABULARY

Diligence: steady, persistent effort

Schemes or imaginations: secret plans or plots

Devise: to invent; to plot

Conflict or discord: disagreement; dispute; controversy

We have learned that in order for God to bless your life now, you must respect and obey your parents. During the time you are at school, your teachers are helping your parents. Therefore, your teachers deserve the same respect that you give your parents. When you do not obey your parents or teachers, you are really rebelling against God. Most young people would say they love God even if they are disrespectful to their parents or teachers.

 What did Christ have to say about this attitude in John 14:21? _____

_____

 Therefore, if you truly love God, what will be your attitude toward your parents and teachers?

_____

True Obedience Comes From Within

Sometimes we obey outwardly but are still rebellious inside. Think about the attitude of the little girl in this story. While driving, Dad noticed that little Judy was standing up in the back of the minivan. "Judy, please sit down! If I stopped suddenly, you'd go right through the windshield." But Judy remained standing. Dad insisted, "Judy, you must sit down! Put on your safety belt."

The little girl dropped to the seat with a frown on her face. "Okay, I'll sit down," she said defiantly, "but I'm still standing up inside."

All of us have had this attitude sometime or another, but we must learn that it is wrong. It is sin. It is also an evidence that the Holy Spirit is not in control.

Life Principle: God wants our hearts—not just our actions.

The following verses will help you see how important the attitude of the heart really is. Read each verse and then summarize what it says about our attitudes.

Proverbs 4:23: ____

____

Proverbs 23:26: ____

____

Matthew 12:30: ____

____

Seven Things The Lord Detests

Read Proverbs 6:16–19. In the chart below, list seven things the Lord detests. From what you learned in lesson eleven explain how Absalom sinned in each area.

God Detests...	How Absalom Sinned
1.	
2.	
3.	
4.	
5.	
6.	
7.	

Now read Proverbs 6:20–23. What should Absalom have done instead so that his life would not have ended in destruction? _____

_____

Give Your Heart To God

What does 2 Chronicles 31:20–21 say about the reasons for Hezekiah's success as the king of Judah? _____

_____

_____

_____

_____

_____

Think about your own relationship to God. To help you, complete the following chart by listing some things you can do to seek the Lord in each of these areas:

Ways I Can Seek The Lord

At home: _____

_____

_____

At school: _____

_____

_____

At church: _____

_____

_____

In my free time: _____

_____

_____

God says, "Give me your heart." Are there still ways you are rebelling against God? If there are such areas, list them below, admit to the Lord you are wrong, and ask Him to help you submit your heart to Him. Yield your heart to the Lord daily, and He will give you the help you need to grow and obey.

_____

_____

_____

LESSON 13
Learning To Stand Alone

Key Verse: 1 Corinthians 15:58

VOCABULARY

Locusts: a type of grasshopper that travels in large swarms

Upright: righteous; morally respectable and honorable

Raiment: clothing

Girdle: a belt, sash, or band that is worn around the waist

Charity: love or good will toward others

John the Baptist is one of the most interesting men in the Bible and an excellent example for your life. He was a man of outstanding courage who was proud to stand out from the crowd as he declared God's message to hostile listeners. We will learn many important lessons from this man's life.

God's Purpose For John The Baptist

First we must realize that God had a purpose for John the Baptist's life even before he was born. It is a good reminder to us that God has a great plan for each of us also.

 First of all, find the word "prophecy" in a dictionary and write the definition here.

_____

_____

Remember, even though we think of prophecy today as speaking about the future, prophecy in the Bible is not always a prediction. Sometimes prophecy in the Bible is simply speaking the message that God has given to His chosen messenger.

 John the Baptist's life was prophesied by God in the Old Testament. According to Isaiah 40:3, what was John's message? _____

_____

 Now read the first part of Luke 3. Which verse says this Old Testament prophecy had been fulfilled? _____

God knows about all of us before we are born. The purpose of John's life was so urgent that God had prepared the Old Testament to foretell his life.

Read Luke 1:16–17 and explain what important purpose God had for John the Baptist's life.

_____

_____

_____

_____

_____

A Godly Difference

John the Baptist's life was definitely different from the crowd. Can you tell that your life is different compared to the kids you know in your neighborhood? Answer the following questions to see what John the Baptist was like:

- He dressed very differently from other men of his day. How did he dress (Matt. 3:4)? _____
  _____
  _____

- What did he eat (Matt. 3:4)? _____

- Whom did he put ahead of himself (John 1:26–27, 29)? _____

John the Baptist was definitely different from other men, but people still followed him. When you are odd, people might laugh at you and not want to be with you. But when you are different in the right sense, you draw others to you. People who want to do right will want to be around you.

Read Matthew 3:5. Did many people want to be around John the Baptist? Where did they all come from? _____

_____

According to verse 6, did the people respond favorably to John? _____ How can you tell?

_____

The Importance Of Good Parents

The right kind of parents will teach you the things that will help you to grow up right. Read Luke 1:5–7 and 13–15. Explain below who John the Baptist's parents were. _____

_____

_____

What kind of people were they? _____

_____

_____

_____

How did God choose to bless them? _____

_____

Be thankful that you have the kind of parents who are concerned enough about your life to send you to a Christian school. They want you to grow in godliness and learn to have strong courage to do right.

> **Life Principle:** God wants us to learn that we don't have to follow the crowd in order to get popularity. Learn to stand for what is right, even if it means standing alone.

Now, of course, God does not want us to dress like John did because we really would look ridiculous today! But He does want us to look right and act right. He wants people to know that because we are Christians, we are different from the world.

Winning Your Race

What does 1 Timothy 4:12 say about the spiritual responsibilities of young people?

_____

_____

_____

Think about each of the areas named in 1 Timothy 4:12. Give examples of how you can demonstrate godliness in each of these.

Areas	How I Can Demonstrate Godliness
In Speech	
In My Life	
In My Love Toward Others	
In My Faith	
In My Purity	

First Corinthians 2:9–10 has a special promise for those who want to be godly in their lives. What does God say about His plans for you in these verses? _____

_____

_____

_____

_____

Dare To Stand

Key Verse: Joshua 24:15

Deciding What Is Really Important

Every Christian must decide who is going to be number one: Self or Christ. If Jesus Christ is really in first place, it is because you have made a conscious decision to submit to Him.

What is most important to you? Are you more interested in…

- What your friends think or what God thinks?
- Listening to your friends or obeying God?
- Getting your own way or being honest?
- Having right now the things your friends have or waiting for God's timing?

John the Baptist made some very important statements about the ideas listed above. What did he say in John 3:27? _____

_____

Explain this verse in your own words. _____

_____

_____

Therefore, what should be your attitude about each of the four areas listed above?

- _____

  _____

- _____

  _____

- _____

  _____

- _____

  _____

How To Choose Friends

Proverbs 1 teaches a very important lesson about following the wrong kind of friends.

 Read verses 10 through 16. Then answer the following questions:

- What will wrong friends try to do? _____

- What is God's warning to you about these friends? _____
  _____

- Why is God so concerned about these things? _____
  _____

- What kind of friends should you choose? _____
  _____

Making Christ more important than everything else means giving your will to God. When you do this, you can be sure that God will begin to bless your life. You will still have problems, but the Lord will always do what is best for you.

Speaking Out Boldly For Right

John the Baptist continually put Christ ahead of himself. This gave him boldness to stand alone for what was right. One time John had to stand before King Herod and speak the truth. Most people would try to say only pleasing things to someone as important as a king, but the Lord gave John the courage to speak out boldly.

 Read the story in Mark 6:17–28 and answer the following questions:

- What had King Herod done wrong in God's eyes (vv. 17–18)? _____
  _____
  _____
  _____

- What did Herodias want to do to John (vs. 19)? _____

- Even though John had spoken boldly against him, what was Herod's attitude (vs. 20)?
  _____
  _____

- Read verses 21–25 and explain the events that led to the death of John the Baptist.
  _____
  _____

_____

_____

_____

_____

- Did Herod want to have John killed (vs. 26)? _____

- Why did he allow it to happen (vv. 26–28)? _____

_____

_____

_____

Do Right Because It Is Right

It is sad to think of someone like John the Baptist dying as he did. And yet we must realize that God allows all things for a purpose in the life of a Christian. John had fulfilled God's purpose for his life, and God wanted him in heaven. Yes, John the Baptist lost his life for having the courage to do what was right. But he had the eternal knowledge that he had done God's will and the eternal blessing that followed.

What did Christ say about John the Baptist in John 5:35? _____

_____

What did He mean by this? _____

_____

Abraham Lincoln was one of the greatest men in our country's history. Humanly speaking, without him, we might not be a complete nation today. God gave him great wisdom, and yet most of the time Lincoln had to stand alone because most men did not agree with him. This must have been very difficult for Lincoln. This is what Lincoln had to say about why it was so important to do right:

"I desire to so conduct the affairs of this administration that if, at the end, when I come to lay down the reins of power, I have lost every other friend on earth, I shall at least have one friend left, and that friend shall be deep down inside me. I am not bound to win, but I am bound to be true. I am not bound to succeed, but I am bound to live up to the light I have."

Life Principle: It is right to do right because it's right!

Winning Your Race

✏️ In what areas of your life do you need to stand alone for what is right?

_____

_____

Read Proverbs 22:1 and answer the questions below.

✏️ Be honest! Check which of the following things you would rather have.

☐ A good name   ☐ Great riches

✏️ What can you do today, through the Lord's strength, to help you have a "good name"?

_____

_____

Unit Four:
Hindrances To The Runner

The decathlon is comprised of ten separate events. The athlete must be capable in each of these areas in order to win the overall competition. This is what makes the decathlon unique. The events are organized into two days of competition.

Each of the events has its own problems and difficulties that need to be overcome. Some of the competitions require speed, some require endurance, some require the ability to jump great lengths or set marks for height, and others require strength. In each event, then, there are particular obstacles to success and areas that need to be overcome so victory can be achieved. The number of different events can be a hindrance in itself since you can become proficient in several areas and yet be defeated in another area.

The Christian life has its own hindrances and problems. The Christian must recognize the areas that may become weaknesses, which will hinder him from achieving victory. The Christian life is not always easy. Life is filled with tribulations and afflictions, and we must learn how to overcome these. We must also learn to recognize how Satan works to influence us and control our lives. Satan is a very real person in the world, and we must be very wise so that we might not allow him to gain a victory in our lives. Finally, since Satan has such great influence in this world, there are many worldly influences that strive for our attention. God wants us to learn the dangers of these influences so that we might be free of evil.

Just as the decathlon athlete cannot achieve victory if he doesn't recognize and overcome the problems in each event, neither can the Christian achieve victory if he doesn't learn how to recognize his enemies and overcome them (Hebrews 12:1). The goal of this unit is to pinpoint the influences that will defeat you and to show you how to have victory over them.

LESSON 15
Acting Like A Fool

Key Verse: Proverbs 1:7

Jezebel—The Queen Of Sin

The name Jezebel is often used as a nickname for an evil and wicked woman, but Jezebel was a real person in the Bible. She was so wicked that we remember her name and use it to describe a foolish and wicked woman even though most people do not know her real story. Jezebel is sometimes called "The Queen of Sin."

Read 1 Kings 16:29–33 and find out the beginning of the story of Jezebel.

Whom did she marry? _____

How do you know he was an important man? _____

_____

Ahab knew that it was wrong in God's eyes to marry someone who did not believe in Him. But to help make his kingdom stronger, he married a heathen woman who worshiped idols.

List phrases from our Bible text that show Ahab's attitude toward God.

_____

_____

_____

_____

_____

A False Religion

Jezebel did not take long at all to make Baal-worship the state religion. This religion was one of the most evil and wicked religions man has ever devised.

Jezebel's religion was false, and the rest of her life was also false, as you will see.

Write how the righteous feel about anything false according to Proverbs 13:5.

_____

God gives us a special warning in Hebrews 3:12. What is His warning concerning false religions?

_____

_____

_____

When people refuse to glorify God, what does God do to them?

- Romans 1:24: He gives them over to _____ .
- Romans 1:26: He gives them over to _____ .
- Romans 1:28: He gives them over to a _____ .

What is the difference between the one true God and any other god (Rom. 1:23)?

_____

_____

Anything that is more important than God is really a kind of idol. What might such things be in your life? _____

_____

_____

Characteristics Of A Fool

Everything about Jezebel's life was false! Look up the following verses in the book of Proverbs, which is a book of wisdom.

✎ What kind of people are really fools according to these verses?

- Proverbs 1:7: _____

- Proverbs 14:8: _____

- Proverbs 14:9: _____

- Proverbs 15:5: _____

- Proverbs 20:3: _____

- Proverbs 29:11: _____

✎ How do Ecclesiastes 5:3 and 10:14 describe a fool? _____
_____

God does not want us to be a fool like Jezebel. He wants us to learn to have wisdom.

Life Principle: If we do not grow in the wisdom of God, we become fools.

The Sin Of Covetousness

✎ Jezebel was very interested in material things. She wanted wealth and was bitterly jealous of what others had. Both she and Ahab were covetous. What does it mean to be "covetous"?
_____
_____

Now read 1 Kings 21:1–4 to learn more about Jezebel and her strong desire for material possessions.

✎ What did Naboth own? _____

✎ Where was it located? _____

✎ What was Ahab's request? _____
_____
_____

✎ What was Naboths' reason for refusing the offer? _____
_____
_____

At this point, had Ahab sinned in the eyes of God? _____

What should Ahab's attitude have been at this point? _____
_____

Now read verse 4 and describe Ahab's attitude. _____
_____

Read verses 5–15. What did Jezebel do in order to get what her husband wanted?
_____
_____
_____
_____

Winning Your Race

What is wrong with the sin of covetousness?
_____
_____
_____

What areas in your life might show that you have a problem with covetousness or jealousy? Are there things that you tend to desire to the point of covetousness? What are they?
_____
_____
_____

How might this hurt your relationship with other people?
_____
_____
_____

LESSON 16
Greed And Covetousness

Key Verse: Exodus 20:17

VOCABULARY

Covetousness: jealously desiring what belongs to someone else

Blaspheming: to express lack of reverence for God

Sackcloth: a garment worn as a sign of mourning or repentance

Fast: abstaining from food for a period of time to seek the Lord, often to seek wisdom or as a sign of repentance

Let's review Proverbs 6:16–19, which lists seven things that are detestable in God's eyes. All of these things apply to the story of Ahab and Jezebel. List them below.

1. _____

2. _____

3. _____

4. _____

5. _____

6. _____

7. _____

As a reminder from our last lesson, use these words in the blanks below.

Baal	pout	Naboth	heart	fool	Ahab	God	vineyard

Jezebel, as we have learned, was one of the most wicked women who had ever lived. She had a sinful, unbelieving _____. Her faith was in _____, an idol, instead of the living _____. Her life was shallow. She married _____ and took his heart from God because her own heart was wrong. She became a _____. Then Ahab saw a _____ that was owned by a man named _____. Ahab wanted to own it. When it was refused him, he became very covetous and began to _____.

The Sin Of Covetousness

When you want something and cannot have it, how does God want you to respond? Read Ephesians 5:20 and 1 Thessalonians 5:16–18. _____

_____

Remember, it is not wrong to desire something, but we need to make sure our desire does not change to covetousness. This is a sin that can lead to greater sins. Read the rest of the story of Naboth and his vineyard in 1 Kings 21, and see the sins into which Jezebel's evil heart led her.

What was Ahab complaining about in verses 5–6? _____

_____

What did Jezebel promise in verse 7? _____

_____

Her mind had already planned wickedness. Read verses 8–10 and explain her plan.

_____

_____

_____

_____

Was the plan carried out (vs. 13)? _____

What happened to Naboth? _____

_____

As soon as Jezebel heard the news, what did she do (vs. 15)? _____

_____

_____

Was Ahab saddened to hear about Naboth (vs. 16)? _____

How did greed cause him to respond to the news? _____

_____

Life Principle: Covetousness or greed is a wicked sin because it keeps you from praising God for what you have.

Ahab and Jezebel had great wealth. They did not need more; however, because of their evil hearts, they let their sin of covetousness build until more sin developed. This sin is important enough for God to have made it a part of the Ten Commandments.

Which verse in Exodus 20 forbids this sin? _____

Jezebel also broke another commandment in Exodus 20. Which verse contains this commandment, and how did Jezebel break it? _____

_____

_____

God's Response To Covetousness

God hates sin, and anyone who behaves wickedly will be dealt with by God. Ahab probably felt that he could do as he wished because he was the king of Israel, but everyone is equal in God's eyes. God used the prophet Elijah to explain to Ahab what would happen because of his sin.

What did the Lord say would happen to Ahab (1 Kin. 21:19)? _____

_____

_____

What was Ahab's response toward God now (vs. 27)? _____

_____

Because of Ahab's humility and repentance before God, how did God respond (vv. 28–29)?

_____

_____

_____

This is a very important lesson. God always knows our hearts. When we sin, and God sees our hearts and finds that we are truly sorry and repentant, He will always forgive us. When He does not see a repentant heart in us, He will have to discipline us to teach us where we are wrong. He is concerned about our heart attitudes because of His love for us.

God did not forget about Jezebel. Her unbelief in God and her covetous heart made her willing to do anything—even lie and cheat to get what she wanted. Unlike Ahab, Jezebel never repented before God.

Jezebel met death in a terrible way just as God had promised. Read 2 Kings 9:30–37.

Describe how Jezebel, the Queen of Sin, died. _____

_____

_____

_____

Winning Your Race

What have you learned from the story of Jezebel?

_____

_____

_____

✎ What is wrong with the sin of covetousness?

_____
_____
_____

✎ What are some ways in which you can be guilty of covetousness?

_____
_____
_____

✎ How can you overcome the sin of covetousness?

_____
_____
_____

✎ When you sin, what attitude does God want to see in your heart?

_____
_____
_____

LESSON 17
Your Enemy, The Devil

Key Verse: 1 Peter 5:8

VOCABULARY

Iniquity: wickedness; sin

Adversary: an opponent; a foe in battle

God wants us to live victoriously as Christians. We also must realize that while we are on earth, we are in a battle. A battle always involves an enemy. Our enemy is Satan or the devil. We can always defeat our enemy through the power of God in our lives, but we need to be aware of who he is and what his tactics are.

Satan's History

First of all, we need to remember that Satan is a created being. He was created by God just as we were. It is important for Christians to realize that Satan will never have the power of God the Creator. His power and abilities only come from God Himself. God always has the ultimate authority and power. The following section explains how a beautifully created being became the enemy of mankind. Isaiah 14:12–15 likely explains a mighty angel's fall into sin when he became Satan.

 Read this passage and answer the following questions:

- Where did the Devil live at first? _____

- Find the phrase that Satan used boastfully five times in verses 13–14 and then explain what he said in the final phrase that shows his overall attitude toward God.

  _____

  _____

- Now explain the attitude of this last phrase in your own words.

  _____

  _____

- What is God going to do to Satan? _____

  _____

  _____

Now read Ezekiel 28:12–19 to learn more about the character of Satan. As the Lord describes the king of Tyre, he is really describing Lucifer.

List at least two phrases in verse 12 that describe what Lucifer was like before he fell from heaven.

_____

_____

In what famous places do verses 13 and 14 say Lucifer was before he fell?

_____

_____

Verse 14 gives another phrase God used to describe Lucifer before he fell. What is it?

_____

Has Lucifer always existed (vs. 15)? _____

Verse 15 describes the change in Lucifer's character. What was he like at first?

_____

How did Lucifer change? _____

According to verse 16, what did God do because of Lucifer's sin?

_____

_____

Verse 17 explains again what caused Lucifer to fall. What was the reason?

_____

_____

_____

God repeats His promise to destroy Satan in verse 18. How does this verse further explain what will happen? _____

_____

Life Principle: Satan was created by God Himself and will always have to submit to the power of God. The Christian can always have victory over Satan, not because of His own strength, but because of God's.

Satan's Activities

 Read each verse given below. In each verse, explain how Satan is described and what he does or wants to do to men as described in the verse.

Satan Is Called:	What Satan Does:
2 Corinthians 4:4	
2 Corinthians 11:14–15	
Ephesians 2:2	
Hebrews 2:14	
1 Peter 5:8	
Revelation 12:9	

Winning Your Race

Pride and arrogance are great sins. God Himself had created Lucifer, yet Lucifer tried to exalt himself above God.

We have to be careful with the same sins. We don't try to take over God's position, but many times pride makes us act as if we don't need God. Think about your own life.

How does the sin of pride evidence itself sometimes in your own life?

_____

_____

_____

Do you ever set your will against your parents or teachers?_____

How do you act when you give in to the sin of pride?

_____

_____

_____

LESSON 18
How Satan Tempts Us

Key Verse: 1 John 2:16

VOCABULARY

Tempt: to invite or entice to do something sinful

Lust or evil desire: an intense or excessive desire to satisfy some physical appetite

Enticement: tempting someone with the hope of reward or pleasure

Satan disguises himself in many ways. His first goal is to keep people from being saved. When someone does become a Christian, his goal is to keep him out of fellowship with God. Satan wants to keep Christians unhappy, rebellious, and defeated.

Satan, The Deceiver

Several Scriptures show ways that Satan disguises himself and tries to deceive us. Write the meaning of the word "deceive" here before you read the verses. (See lesson eleven for help.)

_____

_____

Read 2 Corinthians 11:14. How does Satan masquerade himself? _____

_____

Explain what you think this means. _____

_____

Read 1 Peter 5:8. What is Satan's purpose for us? _____

_____

Explain what you think this means. _____

_____

Three Areas Of Temptation

Look up the word "tempt." What is its meaning? _____
_____

Who wants to tempt us and keep us from enjoying the life God wants us to enjoy? _____

Read 1 John 2:16. In what three areas does the devil tempt us?

1. _____

2. _____

3. _____

Remember these three areas because we are going to learn more about them.

How We Are Tempted

Now read James 1:13–16. Make sure you understand what verse 13 is saying.

Is God the one who tempts you to do evil? _____

If God does not tempt you, how then is temptation brought to your mind?
_____
_____

Read verse 14. Then look up the meanings of the following words:

"Lust" or "evil desire": _____
_____

"Enticement" or "temptation": _____
_____

Now explain how Satan tempts us. _____
_____

Who actually decides whether we sin or not? _____

Now read verse 15. What is the result of evil desires? _____

What is the result of sin? _____

The Example of Eve

Now review from the beginning of this lesson the three ways Satan tempts us. Then turn to the story of how Eve was tempted in Genesis 3:1–6.

✎ What question did Satan ask in order to tempt Eve? _____

_____

_____

_____

This was really a fact, but Satan made it into a question to tempt Eve with the possibility that it really might be all right.

✎ What did Eve say that God had said?

_____

_____

_____

_____

_____

_____

✎ How did Satan respond to tempt her? _____

_____

✎ Satan wanted to tempt her even further. What did he say would happen to her?

_____

Now compare Genesis 3:6 with the three things you wrote from 1 John 2:16. Write which enticement Satan used beside each of the following:

✎ The lust of human desires (the flesh): _____

✎ The lust of the eyes: _____

✎ The pride of life (who one is and what one has done): _____

_____

We know that Eve gave in to the temptation from Satan. She ate of the fruit, and Adam also ate of the fruit. Just as Satan said, their eyes were opened, and they were now able to know the difference between good and evil. The result that Satan did not reveal to them was death. No longer could they have fellowship with God. Instead, they felt fear and guilt for the first time.

What does Romans 5:12 say about the effect Adam's sin had on all of us.

_____

_____

We know that God overcame sin and death by allowing Jesus Christ to die on the cross for our sins and by His being raised from the dead. We also need to learn how to overcome temptation from Satan while we live on earth. Jesus Himself was tempted by Satan, and we can learn how to recognize Satan's ways and how to defeat him by watching our Savior.

Satan's Temptations For Jesus Christ

Christ was tempted by Satan at the beginning of His earthly ministry. Read about this in Luke 4:1–13. Satan tempted the Lord in the same areas in which he tempted Eve. Read the verses and see what Satan used to tempt Christ in each of these areas and how He answered Satan's temptations.

	The Temptation From Satan	How Christ Answered Satan
The Lust Of Human Desires (vv. 3–4)		
The Lust Of The Eyes (vv. 5–8)		
The Pride Of Life (vv. 9–12)		

In each situation, what did Christ use to defeat Satan? _____

Finally, read verse 13. What did Satan finally do? _____

For how long? _____

Do you think that Christ ever had to deal with Satan's temptations again? _____

Do you think that Satan ever completely leaves us alone? _____

Winning Your Race

Apply what you've learned about Satan's strategies and temptations to your own life. Give an example from your life of two temptations in each of these areas.

Lust of human desires (the flesh):_____

_____

Lust of the eyes: _____

_____

Pride of life (who one is and what one has done): _____

_____

LESSON 19
Overcoming Temptation

Key Verse: Romans 8:37

Satan is very smart. He knows how to tempt us in ways that will reveal our weaknesses. Satan might tempt some boys and girls to steal. He might tempt others get angry or even to fight, and others to lie or cheat. Others who would refuse these more obvious sins might be tempted to be proud about their ability to do good things. In every case, Satan knows us well enough to perceive how he can entice us to fall. Therefore, we need to be aware of our own weaknesses. Think about yourself. In what areas do you think Satan might try to tempt you?

_____

_____

Sifted As Wheat

We have spent some time studying Satan because Christ wants us to be very aware of our great enemy. In Luke 22:31, Christ was talking to Simon Peter and explaining what Satan would try to do.

✎ Write what Christ had to say about Satan. _____

_____

_____

✎ Explain what this means in your own words. _____

_____

✎ What specifically did Christ say would happen (vs. 34)? _____

_____

✎ Did Peter ever think this could happen (vs. 33)? _____

✎ Give an example of a time when Satan tried to shake your faith in the Lord.

_____

_____

Read the rest of the story about Satan's sifting of Peter in Luke 22:54–62.

✎ Did Satan win a victory? _____

✎ Now read Luke 22:32. What is Christ's prayer for each of us? _____

_____

Do You Remember?

Let's review some things we have already learned.

Does God ever tempt you? _____

Why does God allow Satan to tempt you? _____
_____
_____

What type of person does God want you to become? _____
_____

Is there ever a good reason to choose Satan's way? _____

With these things in mind, think about the following:

What must we never do for the devil (Eph. 4:27)? _____
_____

Read James 4:7. To whom are we to submit? _____

What must we do to defeat the devil? _____

What is God's promise if we do this? _____

According to 1 John 2:13, can young people ever overcome the devil? _____

God's Promise For You

Read 1 Corinthians 10:12–14 and answer the following questions:

Why shouldn't you ever begin to think that you don't have to worry about Satan's tempting
you? _____

What is common to all people? _____

Who is always faithful? _____

What is God's promise to you when you are tempted? _____
_____
_____
_____

You see, God never tempts you, but He allows Satan to tempt you for a purpose. He wants you to learn to trust Him more. If you never had to choose between right and wrong, you would never have good Christian character. By having to choose the right, God is teaching you to be a strong person inside. A weak person is one who listens to Satan, gives in to temptation, and chooses to do wrong. God cannot build a strong character in someone who continually chooses wrong.

The Christian's Armor

Read Ephesians 6:10–18. What command is given in verse 11? _____
_____
_____
_____

According to verse 11, what is the purpose for this command? _____
_____
_____
_____

According to verse 12, why does this command have to be given? _____
_____
_____
_____
_____

What is this armor that Paul is talking about? Paul does not leave us guessing because he goes on to list the six major pieces of the Christian armor. List these pieces in the blanks below.

Verse 14: _____
_____
_____

• How will knowing God's truth help you in your spiritual battles? _____
_____
_____
_____
_____

✎ Verse 14: _____

- Why is it so important for us to have the righteousness of Christ? _____
_____

✎ Verse 15: _____

- According to this, what is one of our purposes for standing against the devil?
_____

✎ Verse 16: _____

- According to this verse, what is the specific purpose for this shield? _____
_____

✎ Verse 17: _____

- How is this piece of armor described in 1 Thessalonians 5:8? _____
_____

✎ Verse 17: _____

- According to this verse, what is this piece of armor? _____

✎ According to Ephesians 6:13, what are we supposed to do once we have put on all these pieces of armor? _____
_____

Winning Your Race

Knowing these things, explain why the following statement is so important. It is always right to do right because it's right! _____

_____

_____

_____

Young people need to pay particular attention to their relationships with other people, particularly their friends. How we get along with one another is very important to God. He loves each one of us and wants us to learn to love each other in the same way. Therefore, this is definitely an area in which Satan will try to make us fall. Think through some of the things we have been learning as you complete the following exercise.

Match the two parts of each sentence by putting the proper letter in front of the phrase to make the sentences match correctly.

	1. When we have a fight or a problem with a friend,...	A. ...what leads to peace.
	2. People don't always agree,...	B. ...we know Satan will try again in another area.
	3. When we do not fight and can say we are sorry,...	C. ...Satan is tempting us.
	4. Let us therefore make every effort to do...	D. ... he will flee from us.
	5. God promises that if we resist Satan,...	E. ...we are resisting the devil.
	6. After we win a victory over Satan in one area,...	F. ...but God helps them work together.

LESSON 20
Conformity To Christ

Key Verse: Romans 12:2

VOCABULARY

Conformity: becoming like something else; agreement

Transformed: changed into something else in character and appearance

After you have trusted Jesus Christ as your personal Savior, you are no longer the same person. Before, you only had your own sin nature. Now the Spirit of God lives in you. You no longer are on your own—the Holy Spirit will continually try to control your life in order to make your life free from sin and guilt. He wants to make your life peaceful and successful.

The Holy Spirit's Temple

Read 1 Corinthians 6:19–20 and then answer the following questions:

Why does God refer to your body as a "temple"? _____
_____

These verses say that we have been bought for a price. What was the price?
_____
_____

What gives God the right to own you (1 Cor. 7:23)? _____
_____

Therefore, as a Christian, why should your life be glorifying to God? _____
_____

Conformity Or Separation?

Look up the following words and write their meanings below:

- Conformity: _____
  _____

- Separation: _____
  _____

As a review, read Romans 8:29. To whose likeness are we to be conformed?
_____
_____

This verse also says that God has a right to control our lives. You will be conformed either to become a servant of God or a servant of the world and yourself. God knows the evil world system of men and does not want us to have any part of that system. He tells us to separate from it.

To fully understand why God wants us to separate ourselves from the world, let's read some verses that show us what the world is like. Read Romans 1:29–31 and its list the of twenty-one worldly attitudes and activities.

To which of these sins are you most likely to fall prey?
_____
_____

What does 2 Corinthians 6:17 teach about how God wants us to respond to this evil world system? _____
_____
_____

Now look at the end of verse 17 and all of verse 18. God has given us another commandment with a promise. What does He promise if we obey the above commandment? _____
_____
_____

> **Life Principle:** God wants you to separate from the wrong so He might be free to give you the good. He wants to be a Father to you and bless your life.

In The World, But Not Of The World

Christians are God's ambassadors—His messengers—in this world. God chose for His message to be proclaimed to the world through our words and lives. He chose to influence the world by the Holy Spirit living in us. That is one reason your life is very important to God.

What does Romans 12:2 teach about what needs to be taking place in your heart?

_____

_____

_____

Here again God tells us not to be conformed to the world. Explain in your own words from what you have learned what it means to be conformed to the pattern of this world.

_____

_____

_____

God instead wants our lives to be transformed, or changed. Are you capable of making your life Christ-like? _____

Who is capable of making changes inside your mind and heart? _____

What does this verse say that the Holy Spirit wants to test and approve by your life?

_____

_____

Winning Your Race

God wants to help others by using you! God wants to save others by using you! He has chosen to work through His Word and your life.

Be honest. When others observe your life, do they see someone who is conformed to God or to the world? _____

Name some types of activities and some things you should separate from so that God may be free to bless your life. Discuss these things with your class.

- _____
- _____
- _____
- _____
- _____
- _____

Are you willing for God to work through your life? _____

 Are you then willing to separate, or set yourself apart, from the world and those things that will not glorify God? _____

LESSON 21
Separation From Worldliness

Key Verse: 2 Corinthians 6:14

VOCABULARY

Beneficial or expedient: profitable; contributing to good; useful; advantageous

Yoke: a bar or frame used to couple two animals such as oxen at the heads or necks for working together; a clamp that holds two parts together to unite them in position

The books of 1 and 2 Corinthians teach a great deal about separation from the world. Paul wrote these letters to the people of Corinth because of their worldly and sinful practices. He wanted them to understand how much the Lord Jesus had done for them and how important it was for them to live holy lives.

Five Key Verses

Read each of the following verses and summarize the main principle from each.

✏ 1 Corinthians 3:16: _____

_____

✏ 1 Corinthians 6:12: _____

_____

✏ 1 Corinthians 8:9: _____

_____

✏ 1 Corinthians 10:31: _____

_____

✏ 2 Corinthians 6:14: _____

_____

_____

_____

How Do These Apply To Me?

 Now that you have studied each of these verses, read the following situations or problems. Beside each, tell which of the above verses tells you how you should act or respond. (Note: Some of the following may be answered by more than one verse.)

Which Verse Tells You...	
Why you should be a good example to others (such as not using bad or foul language)?	
Why your close friends should be Christians rather than unsaved young people?	
Why you should promise that you will never smoke or abuse alcohol or drugs?	
Why you should be careful to be a good example to others even though you have freedom in Christ?	
Why you should be careful not to watch wrong things on TV or read books with bad words or ideas or put any wrong things into your mind?	
Why you should be careful to eat fruit, vegetables, meat, and bread rather than too much junk food?	
Why you should not do everything your neighborhood friends might ask you to do?	

Are You Sure You Understand?

 We are going to use the same five verses again. To make sure you understand their meanings, explain each verse in your own words and give an example for each verse from your own life.

Verse	Explanation	Example
1 Corinthians 3:16		
1 Corinthians 6:12		
1 Corinthians 8:9		
1 Corinthians 10:31		
2 Corinthians 6:14		

Winning Your Race

If you do not set yourself apart from the world, you are settling for less than God's best for you! Look at the chart below.

Spiritual level	Choosing what I do because God directs me through the Holy Spirit
Moral level	Choosing what I do because I want to do what's right for my own good
Social level	Choosing what I do because of what my friends think
Natural level	Choosing what I do based on what my instincts tell me

On which level are you living now? _____

On which level do you desire to live? _____

Unit Five:
Pressing Toward The Goal

The Olympic games have an interesting history. They originated in Olympia, Greece before the time of Christ in 776 B.C. Even then they were held every four years. All freeborn honorable citizens from Greek states were invited to take part, and later other countries were welcomed to compete in the games. In these early games only men were allowed to compete, and most of the contests were foot races. Later, the pentathlon, a contest in which the contestants took part in five events, was held. These five events included leaping, running, wrestling, throwing the discus, and hurling the javelin. You may recognize that some of these events are a part of today's decathlon.

These first Olympics lasted 1,000 years until 396 A.D. when a Roman emperor put an end to the games. They were revived 1,500 years later in Athens, Greece in 1896. Today amateur athletes from many nations are invited to participate. Track and field events are the most popular events. The Olympics are still held every four years as in ancient times.

Just as the athletes in the Olympic games, none of us is perfect. In a sense, we are all amateurs. And just as the athletes are perfecting their performances for competition, we as Christians are being perfected by Jesus Christ. Pressing toward the goal of becoming Christ-like is one of the goals of this unit. Jesus Christ wants us to learn how to let Him live through us so that we might be conformed to His image.

We will be studying the life of Jesus Christ and His purpose for coming to the earth during the next few weeks. Jesus Christ came to earth to die in our place, shed His own blood for our sins, and then be raised again so that we might have eternal life by believing on Him. But He also came for another purpose. He wanted to teach us principles of how to live with one another. He also wanted us to learn that His life did not begin in Bethlehem. Jesus has always existed, and He will always be with us in eternity.

LESSON 22
The Lamb Of God

Key Verse: John 1:29

VOCABULARY

Passover: a Jewish holiday commemorating the deliverance of the ancient Hebrews from slavery in Egypt

Hyssop: a fragrant flower of the mint family

Lintel: the horizontal crosspiece over a door or a window

When Jesus Christ was born in Bethlehem, the most important prophecies of the Old Testament were fulfilled. In the New Testament, John the Baptist testified about the fulfillment of the major prophecy we will study in this lesson. Read how John the Baptist acknowledged Jesus in John 1:29.

 What did he say? _____

_____

Garments Of Skin For Adam And Eve

God first pointed toward the idea of the Lamb of God being the way to God at the time of Adam and Eve. In the Garden of Eden, Adam and Eve's sin brought a different relationship with God than they had been used to. God immediately had to withdraw His fellowship from them because of the sin they had committed.

God's first reaction to Adam and Eve and to us was a response of love. There was no way that Adam and Eve could restore the relationship they once had with God, but God promised that He would provide a way. In Genesis 3:15, God promised that He would send a Savior to pay for the sin that had come into the people of earth. To show a picture that would point all people to Jesus Christ, the Son of God, who would be slain for our sin, He did something important.

 Explain what God did in Genesis 3:21. _____

_____

_____

Throughout the Old Testament, we find many instances of the importance of sacrificing an animal. The animal that was used in connection with the shedding of blood and making sacrifice for sin was the lamb.

God Substitutes A Ram For Isaac

Earlier in this book, we studied the story of the obedience of Isaac when God commanded Abraham to sacrifice his only son on an altar. At the last moment, God provided a different sacrifice. Read Genesis 22:6–13 to review this part of the story.

What did Abraham do in verse 6? _____

_____

_____

What important question was Isaac concerned about in verse 7? _____

_____

_____

What important answer did Abraham provide in verse 8? _____

_____

_____

What was Abraham prepared to do (vv. 9–10)? _____

What did God provide (vv. 11–13)? _____

According to verse 12, why did God test Abraham in this way? _____

_____

The Passover Lamb

One of the most important events that showed the picture of the lamb as a savior took place in Egypt when Moses was seeking the freedom of the Israelites from the Egyptians. Over and over again, God had brought plagues on Egypt to persuade the Pharaoh to release His people. And again and again, Pharaoh hardened his heart even as the plagues became worse and worse. Nine times God had brought devastation on the land, but Pharaoh was firm in his refusal to let God's people go.

Finally, God brought about the tenth plague, which was preceded by the Passover. The importance of the Passover Lamb is very evident.

✏ Read Exodus 12:21–23 and explain in your own words what God asked the Israelites to do.

_____
_____
_____
_____
_____
_____

✏ What happened that night to the Egyptians (vv. 28–30)? _____

_____
_____
_____

✏ What protected the Israelite homes from the same fate? _____

_____
_____

Jesus Christ, Our Passover Lamb

We have looked at three instances in the Old Testament that speak of the sacrifice of the blood of an innocent and perfect lamb to accomplish a purpose in God's plan. In the Book of Leviticus, God gave the people many, many different laws and rules for how to use the lamb as a sacrifice for sin. In the Old Testament the lamb was only a symbol of the coming Savior who would sacrifice Himself for us by shedding His own blood.

God has taken great care many times in the New Testament to tell us that Jesus Christ is our Passover Lamb. Read the following verses and list how they refer to Christ.

✏ John 1:36: _____

✏ 1 Corinthians 5:7: _____

_____

✏ 1 Peter 1:19: _____

✏ Revelation 5:12: _____

✏ Revelation 13:8: _____

_____

The Fulfillment Of Isaiah 53:7

Isaiah 53:7 is an Old Testament prophecy of all that we have been studying concerning Jesus Christ's purpose on earth. Read the verse and then, beside each phrase below, explain how Christ fulfilled each prophecy.

Prophecy	Fulfillment
He was oppressed.	
He was afflicted.	
He did not open His mouth.	
He was led like a lamb to the slaughter.	
He was silent as a sheep is before His shearers.	

Remember: The sacrificing and shedding of the blood of the lamb in the Old Testament did not take away the sins of the people. When they sacrificed a lamb, they were acknowledging to God that they could not rid themselves of their sins but needed a Savior. The blood of the lamb temporarily covered their sins. They were waiting for Jesus Christ, the Lamb of God, to one day sacrifice Himself and shed His own blood for them.

Key Verse: Matthew 14:14

VOCABULARY

Pharisee: a member of the Jewish religion known for strict adherence to the rites and ceremonies of traditional Jewish law

Palsy: a physical condition marked by loss of power to control the movement of any part of the body

Paralytic: one with a physical condition marked by loss of power to control the movement of any part of the body

Leprosy (leper): a disease marked by slow growing swellings with deformity and loss of sensation of affected areas

Blasphemy: expressing lack of reverence toward God or sacred things

Mute or dumb: lacking the power of speech; silent

Christ's ministry on earth included more than forty miracles that are recorded in the Gospels. A miracle is not a trick or a work of magic. A miracle is an act that cannot be explained in any earthly terms. It has a supernatural, superhuman cause. A miracle can only be explained as an act of God.

These miracles filled a purpose in God's plan. What was the primary purpose according to John 20:30–31? _____

_____

_____

_____

Life Principle: The miracles showed that Jesus Christ was truly God. As God, He had power or control over all things on earth, in hell, and in heaven.

Four Types Of Miracles

There were four types of miracles that Christ performed while He was on this earth.

- Power over death: He raised the dead.

- Power over demons (hell): He cast out demons or evil spirits.

- Power over disease: He healed the sick.

- Power over nature: He showed His power over the seas, the wind, food, fish, etc.

It is also interesting to notice the people's response to the miracles of Christ. Usually, the people's attitudes were different from those of the Pharisees and other religious leaders. As you complete the table below, notice the differences between the responses of these two groups:

Read the following passages. More than one is listed in most cases is because each Gospel often describes the same miracle. Therefore, each reference to a miracle is given for you to check each account for your answer. Describe each miracle, and tell which of the four types of miracles it represents. Finally, describe the response of others to the miracle.

Scripture	Christ's Miracle	Type Of Miracle	The People's Response
Matt. 8:1–4; Mark 1:40–45; Luke 5:12–15			
Matt. 9:1–8; Mark 2:1–12; Luke 5:17–26			
Luke 7:11–17			
Matt. 8:23–27; Mark 4:35–41; Luke 8:22–25			
Matt. 12:9–14; Mark 3:1–6; Luke 6:6–11			
Matt. 8:28–34; Mark 5:1–20; Luke 8:26–39			
John 5:1–16			
Matt. 9:18–26; Mark 5:21–43; Luke 8:41–56			

Scripture	Christ's Miracle	Type Of Miracle	The People's Response
Matt. 14:13–21; Mark 6:30–44; Luke 9:10–17; John 6:1–14			
Matt. 8:5–13; Luke 7:1–10			
Matt. 12:22–30; Luke 11:14–23			
Matt. 14:22–33; Mark 6:45–52; John 6:16–21			
John 9:1–38			
John 11:1–46			
Luke 17:11–19			

The Religious Leaders Respond

From what you have studied, what conclusions can you make regarding the differences in attitudes between the ordinary people and the religious leaders? _____

_____

_____

_____

To better understand why the religious leaders felt this way, read John 11:47–53 and explain their reasons. _____

_____

_____

What did they plan to do (John 11:53)? _____

Christ Shows Us How To Live

Key Verse: John 4:14

Jesus Christ had several purposes in coming to earth. His most important goal was to suffer and die on the cross in our place so that we might be forgiven of our sins. In order that He might prove that He was God and could therefore pay for our sins, He rose from the dead and lives in heaven today. He also performed many miracles to demonstrate His power and deity, as we have already studied.

But Christ also had another purpose for being on this earth. He wanted to teach all of us how to live together and respond to each other. Christ truly loves each person He has created and wants each person to be with Him in heaven if he or she will believe in Him. He wants us to learn to love each other in the same way. That is very difficult for us because of our sinful, fleshly nature. But His life showed us a beautiful example of how our lives ought to be.

Then, as we have learned, after Christ went to heaven, He sent the Holy Spirit to live in us so that we might truly live His life. The fruit of the Spirit begins with the life of Jesus Christ.

List the fruit of the Spirit from Galatians 5:22–23 to remind yourself of the principles God wants to teach you to live by. _____

_____

_____

_____

The Land Of Palestine In The Days Of Jesus

Before we begin to look at some of the ways in which Christ taught us how to live, we need to have an understanding of the geography of the land in which Christ lived and traveled. Look at the map on the next page and notice the three major regions of the land of Palestine.

- Galilee: the northern region
- Samaria: the central region
- Judea: the southern region

Notice also some of the physical features of the land.

- Sea of Galilee
- Jordan River
- Dead Sea
- Mediterranean Sea

Of course, one of the most important things to notice is the names and locations of the major towns and villages. Read the verses below and fill in the blanks with the name of the correct town or village. Then use one of the maps in your Bible to locate that town or village. Write the name of the town beside the correct dot on the map to indicate its location.

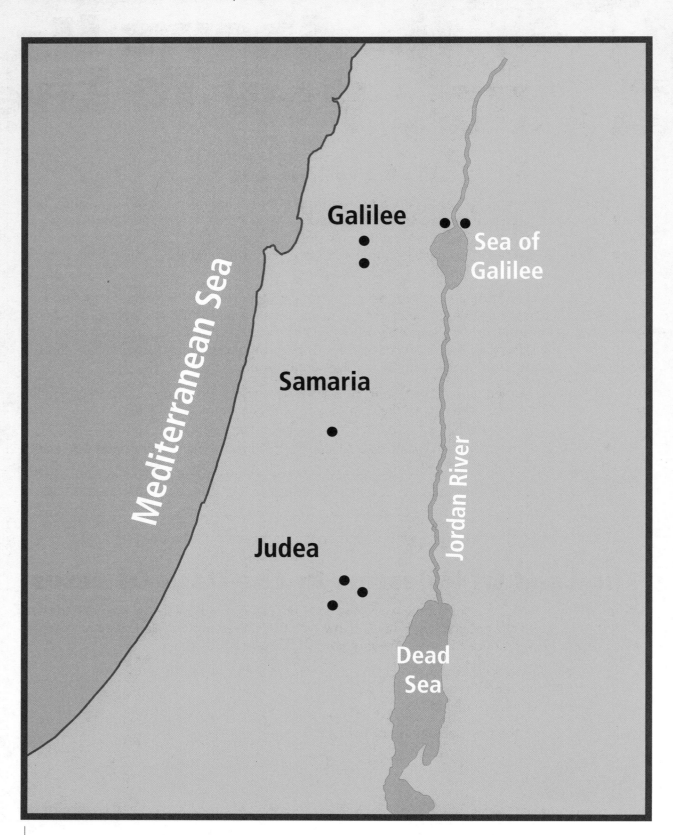

✎ Luke 2:4: Christ was born in _____.

✎ Luke 2:39: Christ lived in _____ from the days of His childhood until He began His ministry.

✎ Matthew 4:13: When Christ left Nazareth, He went to the city of _____ and began to preach.

✎ John 2:1: Christ performed His first miracle in _____.

✎ John 4:5: Christ met the Samaritan woman in _____, a city of Samaria.

✎ Luke 9:10: The hometown of Philip, Peter, and Andrew where Christ fed five thousand was _____.

✎ John 12:1: Mary, Martha, and Lazarus lived in _____.

✎ John 12:12: Christ was arrested, tried, and crucified in the city of _____.

Christ Meets The Samaritan Woman

One of the most beautiful examples of how we should treat one another is found in the story of the Samaritan woman. Christ had left Jerusalem and was planning to return to Galilee. Most Jewish travelers between Judea and Galilee traveled by the Jordan River in order to stay completely out of Samaria. Notice the location of these places on your map. You will see the great distance that needed to be traveled on foot in order to avoid contact with the people of Samaria. The Jews were suspicious of and hated the Samaritans and wanted nothing to do with them. But Christ wanted to demonstrate His love to all peoples, not just the Jews. He also wants to teach us how to respond to people who are different than we are or who have problems.

Read John 4:3–18 and fill in the blanks to complete the following story:

🖉 Christ came to a city in Samaria named _____. He was weary from His traveling and decided to rest by _____. A Samaritan woman came to the well to draw water, and Christ asked her to _____. He was alone because His disciples had gone to the city to buy _____. The woman told Him that she didn't understand why He had asked her for a drink because _____ _____.

Christ then told her that if she really understood to whom she was talking, she would have asked Him for _____ water.

🖉 The woman did not understand what He was referring to, so Christ tried to explain. He said that everyone who drinks this water would be _____, but whoever drinks the water He would give him would never _____. He said that the water He would give would become a spring of water welling up to _____.

🖉 Christ then asked her to call her _____. When she said she had no husband, He told her she had had _____.

🖉 Later, Christ revealed to her that He was the Messiah. In verses 28 and 29, we see that she went to the city and told the people that she had met a man who had told her _____ _____. She told them she thought this was the _____. Then in verse 39, we find that many of the _____ believed in Him because the woman testified that _____ _____.

This story tells us many things about the compassion and love of Jesus Christ.

- First we see that Christ has compassion for unbelievers. The Jews would never have wanted a Samaritan to be saved, but Christ did.

- Then, we know that Christ saw the sinfulness of this woman, but He loved her just the same. He wanted to help her change her life.

- We also see that Christ takes time for people in everyday situations. He is interested in our smallest problems and tries to help us where we are. He met the woman at the well while she was drawing water.

A New Way Of Life

Christ lived a life that was different from any other person who has ever walked on the earth. He did not handle problems the way most people do. The reason no one else has ever set the perfect example Jesus Christ did is because we all have a sin nature. Christ did not have a sin nature. He was a man, but He did not have a sinful, fleshly nature. He did not ever sin.

> **Life Principle:** When we receive Christ as our Lord and Savior, the Holy Spirit lives within us, and we have a spiritual nature. Now we can learn to live as Christ did.

To see some of the differences in the way people normally respond and the way Christ wants us to learn to respond, we will look at four examples that compare the natural way of man under the Old Testament law with Christ's way under grace.

Listed below are some of the natural attitudes of man. Then beside each is a Scripture reference in which Christ tells us to respond in a way that is different from the natural way. Read the verses and tell how Christ wants us to respond.

Natural Attitudes Of Man	Spirit-controlled Attitudes
Get even with anyone who wrongs you.	Matthew 5:38–39:
Hate your enemies, curse those who curse you, and do evil things to those who hate you.	Matthew 5:43–44:
Do your righteous acts before others so that all may see your unselfishness.	Matthew 6:1–4:
Pray only when others can see and hear you so they will think you are spiritual.	Matthew 6:5–7:

Winning Your Race

There are many other areas in which Christ wants us to learn to respond to others with spiritual attitudes, but look again at the four areas we have just discussed. Think of an example from your own life in one of the areas in which you could have responded as a natural man, but you instead responded as Christ taught you.

Give the details of your own life example.

_____

_____

_____

LESSON 25
Christ-Like Attitudes

VOCABULARY

Beatitude: a statement concerning perfect blessedness or happiness

Poor in spirit: being emptied of selfish desires and filled with Christ's desires

Mourn: to feel deep sorrow

Meek: humble and patient

Hunger and thirst for righteousness: a great desire to become more like Christ

Merciful: withholding harm from someone who is guilty of an offense

Pure in heart: having thoughts and attitudes that are clean and unhypocritical

Peacemakers: those who want men to be at peace with God and others

Persecuted for the sake of righteousness: injured or attacked for being like Christ

Learning From Christ's Teachings

Many times in God's Word, Christ teaches us how to deal with circumstances and how to respond to others. One of the best and most beautiful examples of this is found in the first portion of the Sermon on the Mount, which is called the Beatitudes. Read Matthew 5:1–12. These are sometimes called the "be-attitudes" because they relate not so much to what Christ wants us to do (our actions) as to what He wants us to be (our attitudes). Complete the following chart using the statements Christ gave concerning how to be "blessed" (truly happy) in Matthew 5.

Christ-like Attitude	Matthew	Promise
	5:3	
	5:4	
	5:5	

Christ-like Attitude	Matthew	Promise
	5:6	
	5:7	
	5:8	
	5:9	
	5:10	

Learning From Christ's Life

Life Principle: Christ wants us to look at His life to help us learn how to respond to life situations for ourselves.

Read the following verses to see how Christ responded to others:

How did Christ respond to those closest to Him—His disciples?

- Matthew 13:10–11; Mark 6:47–51: _____
  _____
  _____
  _____

How did Christ respond to those who refused to believe in Him?

- Matthew 13:53–58: _____
  _____
  _____

How did Christ respond to people in general?

- Matthew 14:15–21: _____
  _____

How did Christ respond to God?

- John 5:30: _____
  _____

Winning Your Race

It does no good for us just to learn what the Beatitudes (Christ-like attitudes) are. Christ wants us to allow the Holy Spirit to use them in our lives. Below, rename each Beatitude and then give an example of how you can practice that attitude in your own life.

Name The Beatitude	Give An Example For Your Life

LESSON 26
The Crucifixion

Key Verse: Matthew 27:22

VOCABULARY
Flog or scourge: to beat severely; lash
Insult or deride: to make fun of; to laugh at scornfully; to ridicule

In this lesson we are going to look at the most important events that have ever taken place. Without these—Jesus Christ's death and resurrection—we would have no hope of heaven. Neither would there be a purpose for our life on earth.

Christ Knew Everything That Was Going To Happen

Before we look at the events, we need to remind ourselves that none of these events took place by accident. Christ Himself knew in detail all that was to happen. He knew that through these events, He would fulfill His unique purpose for living on earth.

 The following four examples show the foreknowledge He had for these events.

Verses	Evidence Of Christ's Foreknowledge
Luke 18:31–34	
Luke 22:7–13	
Luke 22:31–34, 54–62	
John 13:21–27; 18:1–5	

The Six Trials Of Christ

We cannot study the death of Christ without studying the great sufferings He endured so that we might have life everlasting. First of all, after His betrayal by Judas, Christ was taken and tried illegally six times.

 Fill in the chart below to find out who tried Him and what their responses were.

Verses	The Judge	The Response
John 18:12–14, 19–24		
Matthew 26:57–68		
Luke 22:66–23:2		
Luke 23:3–7		
Luke 23:7–12		
Luke 23:13–25		

Life Principle: Jesus Christ was condemned to die even though no one could righteously accuse Him of doing anything wrong.

The Sufferings Of Christ

Pilate had simply given in to the demands of the people and religious leaders. Study the following verses to see all that Jesus Christ suffered:

Verses	Who Did It?	What Was Done?
Matthew 27:24–26		
Matthew 27:27–31		
Luke 23:35		

Christ was tortured so much that by the time He was crucified, he could not be recognized. The following verses explain some of the ways He was tortured.

Read each verse and write the type of torture that is mentioned.

- John 18:22: _____ _____

- Luke 22:63–64: _____ _____

- Matthew 26:67: _____ _____ _____ _____

- Matthew 27:26: _____ _____

- Matthew 27:29: _____ _____ _____ _____

- Matthew 27:30: _____ _____ _____ _____

- Matthew 27:35: _____ _____

At the time of Christ's death, many supernatural events took place. Study Matthew 27:45–54 and see how many of these miracles you can find. Even at His death, Christ showed that He had the power of God.

_____
_____
_____
_____
_____
_____

Key Verse: Matthew 28:5-6

On Sunday morning, three days after the death and burial of Christ, some women went very early to the tomb in the garden. One of these women was Mary Magdalene, another was also named Mary, and the third was named Salome. They were bringing some fragrant gums and spices to place in the wrappings upon the body of Jesus. And as they went, they wondered with each other who would roll the stone away from the entrance of the tomb (Mark 16:3).

When they came to the cave, they saw that the seal was broken, the stone was rolled away, and the soldiers who had been on guard were gone. There stood the tomb of Jesus open! They did not know that before they came to the tomb, there had been an earthquake and that an angel had come down from heaven and rolled away the stone. The soldiers had already fled.

 The angel sat on the stone that he had rolled back. His clothes were as white as snow. Seeing Him, the women were filled with fear. Then the angel told them not to be _____ that Jesus was missing because he was risen from the dead (Matt. 28:5–6). Then he told them to go quickly and tell the _____ that Christ had risen from the dead (Matt. 28:7).

Life Principle: Christ's life did not end when He was crucified and buried. Three days later He was alive again!

Christ Appeared To People After His Resurrection

Many do not believe in Christ's resurrection. They willingly believe that Christ lived and that He was a great man, even a prophet. They may also believe that He should not have been crucified because He was not guilty of anything. But they refuse to believe that He was resurrected from the dead.

It is important then to see how many times Christ showed Himself alive to those who knew He had died. The fact of His death is certain—and the fact that He arose from the dead is just as certain. Read the following verses and write the names of the people to whom Christ appeared after His resurrection:

✎ Mark 16:9: _____

✎ Matthew 28:8–10: _____

✎ Luke 24:13–15: _____

✎ Luke 24:34: _____

✎ John 20:19–25: _____

✎ John 20:26–29: _____

✎ John 21:1–14: _____

✎ Matthew 28:16–20: _____

✎ 1 Corinthians 15:6: _____

✎ 1 Corinthians 15:7: _____

✎ Acts 1:3–9: _____

✎ 1 Corinthians 15:8: _____

Christ's Ascension To Heaven

Read Acts 1:6–11. This was the final time the apostles saw Christ on this earth. This was a very important moment for all of us because at this time Christ made several promises.

✎ List the promises made by Christ and the two angels in these verses.

- _____

- _____

- _____

- _____

The Names Of Christ

Jesus Christ has many names given to Him. Each name has a very special meaning.

 Read the verses listed below and fill in the correct name. The meaning is given beside each name.

Verse	Name	Meaning Of Name
Matthew 1:21		Savior
Luke 9:20		Son of God
John 1:29		the perfect sacrifice
John 8:58		He who always lives
John 15:13–14		one who loves
John 20:16		teacher, Lord
1 Timothy 6:15		ruler forever
Revelation 1:17		beginning and end of all things

Winning Your Race

 Christ was on earth forty days after His resurrection. Why do you think it was so important that so many saw Him during this time?

_____

_____

_____

Read 1 Corinthians 15:12–20. Then in your own words explain why the resurrection of Christ is important for your own life. What hope does it provide for you?

_____

_____

_____

Key Verse: Acts 1:8

V O C A B U L A R Y

Sinful nature or "in the flesh": human nature without the Spirit of God and dominated by sin

Carnal: pertaining to the body as the center of desires and appetites; opposed to that which is spiritual

Christ, Our Perfect Example

The life of Jesus Christ had a wonderful effect on the lives of all those who came in contact with Him. He was a perfect example of the life God wants us all to live.

✎ He always loved everyone, even when they hurt and abused Him. What was Christ's attitude toward the people who crucified Him (Luke 23:34)? _____

_____

_____

Christ's purpose was to meet the needs of others and help them. He taught them how to treat one another, He healed the sick and lame, He showed people how to be saved, and He taught forgiveness and love.

His twelve disciples were with Him constantly, as were many others who followed Him, but something was missing. The disciples could not be like Christ while He was still here. He had the power of God within Himself (because He was God), but no one else had the Holy Spirit within them.

✎ To learn more about the attitudes of people who do not have the Holy Spirit, find Matthew 26 and see some of the reactions of those closest to Him. Read verses 47–56 and describe what is happening. _____

_____

_____

_____

How did one of the disciples react in verse 51? _____

_____

This attitude shows impulsive anger. How did Christ respond in verse 52 (see also Luke 22:51)?

_____

_____

What did His attitude show?

1. _____

2. _____

How did the disciples respond to Christ's arrest in verse 56? _____

_____

How do you think they felt? _____

_____

The Coming Of The Spirit

Christ is always a perfect example of the life God wants us to live. But we have seen that even with this example before us, we cannot live this kind of life on our own. This is because we need the power of God inside us to transform, or change, our thoughts and attitudes just as Christ was led by the Holy Spirit of God.

The Bible teaches that those who are not filled or controlled by the Holy Spirit are living according to their fleshly desires or the sinful mind. Read about these terms in Romans 8:5–8.

One of the main purposes for Christ's resurrection and ascension into heaven was for the Holy Spirit to come and live within us. Christ explained this to His disciples in Acts 1:8.

What were they to receive? _____

How would they receive it? _____

What would be the result? _____

_____

What happened as soon as Christ spoke these things? _____

_____

Peter Before The Spirit Came

The story of Peter is a good example of the difference the power of the Holy Spirit can make in our lives. Read Luke 22:54–62 to see what Peter was like when Christ was still on the earth.

When Christ was arrested, where did Peter follow? _____

_____

What did Peter say when he was pointed out as being a follower of Christ?

_____

_____

How many times did he give this same response? _____

When Peter realized he had failed the Lord, what did he do? _____

_____

_____

Peter wanted to do right. He loved the Lord and told Him that he would always stand by Him. But he failed because he was living according to his fleshly desires and did not have the power of God inside him. He was angry, bitter, and afraid to speak the truth. Afterward he hurt inside and wept over what had happened.

Peter After The Spirit Came

Life Principle: Ten days after Christ ascended into heaven, the Holy Spirit came to earth and filled those who believed in Christ.

When the Holy Spirit came, all believers had the power of God in their lives to help them become what He wanted them to be. Now, instead of having Christ as an external example, we have the Holy Spirit inside of each of us.

Now notice Peter's life. No longer was he afraid and frustrated. From Acts 2:14 copy the words that tell how Peter began his first sermon. _____

_____

_____

✎ Acts 2:38 shows the new courage Peter had to speak out for Christ. What was Peter's great message? _____

_____

_____

_____

✎ Later in Acts 4:18–20, what were Peter and John commanded to do? _____

_____

✎ How did Peter and John respond? _____

_____

_____

✎ In your own words, explain the reason for the change in Peter's life. Remember the way he was at the time Christ was crucified and how he was now. What effect did the Holy Spirit have in his life? _____

_____

_____

✎ Peter wanted to be used of God. But he only became useful to God as he allowed the Holy Spirit to control and transform his life. How is the Holy Spirit transforming your life?

_____

_____

_____

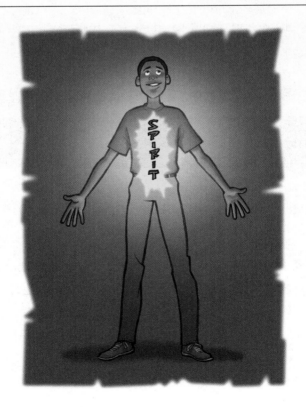

Unit Six:
The Prize Is Won

In the ancient Olympics, those who won in competition were crowned with olive branches as a sign of victory. Today, winners are rewarded in special ceremonies with gold, silver, and bronze medals worn around their necks.

The gold medal won for the decathlon is in many ways the most prestigious of the awards in the Olympic games. Throughout the history of the Olympics, the winner of the decathlon has been thought to be the world's greatest athlete.

For Christians, a time will come when we will receive rewards from the Lord. Just as athletes are rewarded individually by name for the results of their performances, so will God reward us personally for what He accomplished through us.

We will receive crowns in heaven because of our faith in Jesus Christ. He will give us an ultimate victory over all our enemies. Christians will be victorious because of Jesus Christ and what He has done.

This future time will also be a time of great tribulation and turmoil on the earth that will be worse than anything that has been seen before. This unit will teach you about these coming events. The unsaved will be rewarded according to the righteous judgment of God, and the Christians will be given heavenly rewards far beyond anything we can comprehend while we are on earth. It will be a time of judgment for the unsaved and a time of rejoicing and victory for the Christian.

What Will Happen In The Future?

Key Verse: Revelation 1:3

VOCABULARY

Defile: to make corrupt or unclean

Abomination: a loathsome, detestable thing

The Beginning And The End

The book of Revelation is the final chapter in the story of man on earth. It is Satan's plan to control the earth. The book of Revelation tells of Christ's complete victory over Satan. The events in this book (beginning with chapter 4) are still in the future, but the fact of their happening is sure.

Revelation is an "unveiling" of the glory of Jesus Christ, especially as it relates to future events. It finishes the story that was started in Genesis, the book of beginnings. Let's compare what God did in Genesis with what things will be like in the future according to the book of Revelation.

Genesis	Revelation
The heaven and earth were created.	21:1
God dwelt with Adam and Eve until the Fall.	21:3
With the Fall, sin brought death, sorrow, and pain.	21:4
Sin in the world brings decay and destruction.	21:5

Genesis	Revelation
The first marriage was held. Eve was Adam's bride.	21:9 Who is the Lamb? Who is the bride?
The Garden of Eden was a perfect place. Adam and Eve had to leave because of sin.	21:10–21
The sun and moon give us light.	21:23–24
God began time, giving us day and night.	21:25
Sin became a great force on the earth.	21:27
Satan is the prince of this world.	22:3–5

Ever since his meeting with Adam and Eve, Satan has attempted to separate man from fellowship with God. For the most part, he has been victorious. But we can see that the time will come when he will utterly and finally fall. Jesus Christ will be victorious.

Long ago, God told the prophet Isaiah that Jesus Christ would be the ruler. By what names did God prophesy that Christ would be known in Isaiah 9:6–7?

_____

_____

What would His kingdom be like? _____

_____

_____

God's Promises Will All Come True

We have already studied about the prophecies concerning the birth, life, and death of Christ. We saw that many details about Christ's life were written in the Old Testament thousands of years before Christ was born. Every prophecy came true.

In the book of Jeremiah, you will find a promise God made to the nation of Israel about six hundred years before Christ was born. The Israelites had rebelled against God again and again, and God allowed them to be scattered all over the world. Palestine, their homeland, was taken by other nations. The Jewish people suffered severe and terrible persecution for over 2,000 years but always remained strong people. From 1939–1945, during the Second World War, the persecution reached a climax. Germany's ruler, Adolf Hitler, sent six million Jews to their deaths. But the Jews are still God's chosen people, and Palestine is God's promised land for them.

He made a promise to His people through the prophet Jeremiah. Read Jeremiah 30:3. What was God's promise to His people? _____

_____

_____

Over two thousand years later, in 1948, God was still honoring His Word. The Jewish people were allowed to return to Palestine. They have again established their nation. Although this is not the final completion of God's promise that Israel will return and possess her land, this could be part of the beginning of Israel's final restoration.

> **Life Principle:** Many of the prophecies in Scripture have yet to be fulfilled. We can count on the fact that they will all come true. God always keeps His promises.

Read Isaiah 46:9–10 and think through these verses.

What are we to remember? _____

Why is God the only one who could bring these things to pass? _____

_____

How can we know that ancient prophecies not yet fulfilled will come to pass?

_____

_____

_____

The Revelation Of Jesus Christ

Revelation 1 is truly a "revelation of Jesus Christ." He is the central figure in this chapter as it sets the stage for the entire book.

Read Revelation 1 and identify at least twelve truths that this passage reveals about Christ.

- _____
- _____
- _____
- _____
- _____
- _____
- _____
- _____
- _____
- _____
- _____
- _____

Winning Your Race

We are beginning our study of future things. Read Revelation 1:3.

As you study prophecy, what three things does God want you to do to be blessed by Him?

1. _____

2. _____

3. _____

Why are we to do these things? _____

LESSON 30
Christ Returns For His Own

Key Verse: 1 Corinthians 15:51

VOCABULARY

Shameful or vile: unworthy; disgraceful; morally despicable

Deceitful: misrepresenting the truth

Rapture: a snatching away; the event when Christ will take all living and dead Church saints to be with Him in heaven

Diverse or divers: not alike; having various forms or qualities

Pestilence: a destructive, highly infectious disease that spreads swiftly

The Bible is the only book that has prophesied future events in so much detail and without error. Hundreds of God's prophecies have already come to pass. Most were recorded so long before the events actually came to pass that man's mind could never have imagined them.

 Read 2 Peter 1:21. Explain how these prophecies came to be written.

_____

_____

The Rapture Of The Church

Certain events will happen before the Lord brings the events of Revelation 6–22 to pass. The first event is the Rapture of the Church. The word "rapture" is never used in the Bible, but it means "a snatching away." Christ will "rapture" or "snatch away" all those who have trusted Him as Savior. Find out how this will happen in 1 Corinthians 15:51–52 and 1 Thessalonians 4:15–18.

 Describe what will happen in your own words.

_____

_____

_____

_____

_____

What will happen to our bodies when this happens (Phil. 3:20–21)?

_____

_____

What then is the blessed hope for the Christian (Titus 2:12–13)?

_____

_____

The Judgment Seat Of Christ

After the Christians have been taken to heaven at the time of the Rapture, a very important event will occur. All Christians will stand at the Judgment Seat of Christ.

According to 2 Corinthians 5:10 what is the purpose of the Judgment Seat of Christ?

_____

_____

_____

_____

This will not be a fearful time for believers because we will not be judged for our sins. Hebrews 10:17 tells us _____

_____ .

Now read 1 Corinthians 3:12–15 and find out exactly what will take place at the Judgment Seat.

Can gold, silver, and costly stones be burned up? _____

Can wood, hay, and stubble burn? _____

Which foundation then does God want you to build upon? _____

_____

What do these represent? _____

_____

What will God use to reveal whether your works are built on Christ or not? _____

This is a symbol of God's purifying judgment.

What will be the result of those things that are not burned up? _____
_____

What will be the result of those things done in the flesh? _____
_____

Though your works be burned, do you have to worry about suffering or being destroyed yourself? _____

Do you have to worry about losing your salvation? _____

Winning Your Race

We have already studied about what heaven is going to be like for us. How can you be sure these things are true?

Think about the reasons why you should let Christ use your life now to do good works. Number the following in the order in which you think they are important:

_____ To have your works live forever

_____ To teach others about Christ

_____ To receive rewards in heaven

_____ To show our thankfulness for His great love for us

_____ To make sure you'll be in heaven one day

_____ (Your own reason)

_____
_____

Since it is sure that Christ will return for us, we need to think about our own lives. We need to let Christ use us now to witness and be an example to others.

Why do you think these things are important?

_____
_____
_____

LESSON 31
The Tribulation

Key Verse: Matthew 24:21

VOCABULARY

Martyr: one who is put to death for standing up for a religious belief; one who makes a great sacrifice for the sake of his or her principles

Just: morally and legally right

The Day Of God's Wrath

We have learned that the time will come when all born-again Christians will be taken from the earth to meet Christ in the air. After the Christians have left the earth, all the unsaved will be thrown into the worst times the world has ever known.

Read Matthew 24:21–24 and answer the following questions about the terrible times to come:

What name is given to those times? _____

_____

Describe what those times will be like. _____

_____
_____
_____
_____

What will false Christs and false prophets do to fool the people? _____

_____

If these things are not done by the power of God, by whose power will they be done?

_____

How does Daniel 12:1 describe that time period? _____

_____

_____

Remember, God does not allow the Tribulation to come without good warning. For 2,000 years God has wanted people to accept His Son, Jesus Christ, but the world has left God out of its plans. God has always been patient with this rejection.

> **Life Principle:** For 2,000 years, in His Word, God has told all of us—both Christians and unsaved—of the time of tribulation to come on the earth.

Just as God told people about Christ before He was born, so He is also telling the world about the judgment time before it comes. Just as God kept His promise about Christ, so He will also keep His promise concerning the judgment.

The Seven Seals

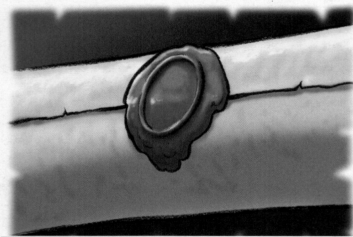

The Tribulation will begin after the true church has been taken away. Beginning in Revelation 6, there is a detailed description of what will actually take place during this Tribulation, which will last seven years. During this period of seven years, God will pour out His wrath on mankind and this earth.

Revelation 6 tells about the seven seals and shows us how man will respond to them. The seven seals are outlined below. Fill in the blanks for yourself.

Seal #1 (6:1–2):	The forces of evil will be set loose.
Seal #2 (6:3–4):	
Seal #3 (6:5–6):	
Seal #4 (6:7–8):	_____ of the people of the earth will be killed.
Seal #5 (6:9–11):	Some of those who accept Christ during the Tribulation will be martyred. Write the meaning of the word "martyr" here.

Seal #6 (6:12–17):	List at least five things that will happen next.
	1.
	2.
	3.
	4.
	5.
Seal #7 (8:1):	What will happen when the seventh seal is opened?

But all of this is only the calm before even greater tribulation. All of heaven is waiting breathlessly because now God will allow Satan to do his last work on earth. It is now time for the judgment of the seven trumpets.

The Seven Trumpets

After the seventh seal is opened, the seven trumpets are blown. These trumpets reveal the wrath God brings upon man. Read the following verses to see what happens on the earth.

Explain the events that will come to pass.

Trumpet #1 (8:7)	
Trumpet #2 (8:8–9)	
Trumpet #3 (8:10–11)	
Trumpet #4 (8:12)	
Trumpet #5 (9:1–6)	
Trumpet #6 (9:13–21)	Revelation 9:13–21 states that the sixth trumpet will bring a great army of horsemen to slay one-third of the population of the earth.
Trumpet #7 (11:15–19)	The seventh trumpet will bring forth even greater wrath on the earth when the seven bowls are opened (16:1–21). We will learn about these in our next lesson. We will also be studying about the Antichrist who will demand worship from the world.

Winning Your Race

Read Romans 1:18–23 to review the attitude of the people on earth toward God. As you read these verses, think about those things that will come to pass during the Tribulation.

Why will God be just in allowing these events to happen during the Tribulation?

_____

_____

Read Revelation 3:10. What does this verse say about whether or not we as believers will have to endure these judgments of God's wrath?

_____

_____

_____

The Antichrist

Key Verse: 2 Thessalonians 2:3

VOCABULARY

Antichrist: the great enemy of Christ during the Tribulation who will be controlled by Satan

Delusion: a false belief or opinion

Saints: those who are assured of heaven because they have received Jesus Christ as their Lord and Savior

The World's Great Leader

During the Tribulation, God will allow Satan to give great power to an enemy of Christ, who will become the world's leader. This is the Antichrist, who will take the place of Christ for the people of the earth. He is "anti" (against) Christ. He will be completely controlled by Satan. Read Daniel 11:36–37. The Antichrist is referred to as "the king" in this passage.

What will be his attitude toward God? _____

_____

_____

Now read 2 Thessalonians 2:3–12 and answer the following questions about the Antichrist:

• What are two names that are used for the Antichrist (vs. 3)? _____

_____

_____

• How will this man present himself to the people (vs. 4)? _____

_____

_____

_____

• How will the Antichrist deceive the people (vv. 9–10)? _____

_____

- Who will give him the power to do these things (vs. 9)? _____

- How do you know that God will still be in control (vv. 10–11)? _____
_____
_____

Using The Power Of Satan

Now read Revelation 13 and see what else the Antichrist will do through the power of Satan.

How strong will his power be, and who will worship him (vv. 7–8)? _____
_____
_____
_____

Now because of the great power of the Antichrist, certain other things will happen in the world. List them after reading the verses below in Revelation 13.

- 13:13: _____
_____

- 13:14: _____
_____
_____

- 13:15: _____
_____

- 13:16–17: _____
_____

If you do not have the mark, what will be the result? _____
_____

The Seven Bowls

We have already begun to see the wrath and justice of God poured out on a world that has rejected Him. The seven seals showed the beginning of the Tribulation. Then the seven trumpets revealed even greater wrath as much of the world's population was destroyed. Now we are going to learn about the final wrath of God upon the earth. Read Revelation 16 and write what will happen as each bowl is poured out.

Bowl #1 (16:1–2):	
Bowl #2 (16:3):	
Bowl #3 (16:4–7):	
Bowl #4 (16:8–9):	
Bowl #5 (16:10–11):	
Bowl #6 (16:12):	
Bowl #7 (16:17–21):	

What will be the attitude of people during this time (16:9, 11)? _____

_____

_____

Is God just in allowing these things to happen? _____ Why (16:5–7)? _____

_____

_____

The Saints In Heaven

The seven seals, the seven trumpets, and the seven bowls show the power of God released against all the followers of the Antichrist. We have seen that there will be plagues even worse than those in Egypt.

During the time that these things are taking place on the earth, the saints will be rejoicing with Christ in heaven and receiving the reward for their service on the earth. Who are these saints?

_____

_____

Read Revelation 19:1, 5–6. What are the saints doing in heaven during the Tribulation on earth? _____

During this time, Christ will reward us according to our work on earth. The rewards will be crowns. Read the following verses and describe the crowns He will give us:

- 1 Corinthians 9:25: This crown is given to those who do not indulge the body. This crown is incorruptible, which means that it lasts _____ .

- 1 Thessalonians 2:19: This crown is Paul's opportunity to rejoice because of people who became believers through his ministry. When would his rejoicing be fully realized? _____

_____

- 2 Timothy 4:8: This crown is given to faithful and loyal Christians who are looking forward to a special event. For what event have they longed? _____

  _____

  What crown will they receive? _____

- James 1:12: This crown is promised to those who show their love for the Lord by persevering under trials. It is the crown of _____.

- 1 Peter 5:4: This crown is given to those pastors (elders) who are good examples and who care for the people in their churches and teach them properly. These men receive the crown of _____

Christ Returns And Reigns

Key Verse: Matthew 24:30

VOCABULARY

Theocracy: a government in which God Himself is the ruler

Justice or right: fairness in administering the law

The Second Coming Of Christ

We have studied about the terrible judgments that will take place on this earth during the Tribulation. What event will occur to end this seven-year period of the pouring out of God's wrath?

Read Matthew 24:29–30 to find out. _____
_____
_____

This is called the second coming of Christ. This time the Lord will come to the earth. At the time of the Rapture, we will be caught up in the air to meet Christ there. The Second Coming of Christ will usher in the final battle of the Tribulation. This great battle is called the Battle of Armageddon.

To understand the differences between Christ's first and second comings, answer the following questions.

In what form did Christ come when He came to the earth the first time? _____
_____

Describe how He will come when He comes to the earth the second time. (See Rev. 19:11–16.)
_____
_____
_____

What is Christ called in Revelation 19:13? _____

What is Christ called in Revelation 19:16? _____

_____

Now read Revelation 19:19. Who is going to be at war against the Lord? _____

_____

_____

This verse also says they will be at war against His army. Who do you think will be in Christ's army?

_____

_____

The Battle Of Armageddon

Man always tries to do without God. Now, as we have been seeing in Revelation, God will let man come to the end of himself during the Tribulation.

Man's only way to solve problems throughout the ages has been through war.

The last battle, the Battle of Armageddon, will be the worst battle the people on earth have ever seen. The following passages from the book of Revelation will explain the results of this battle.

Where will this battle take place (16:16)? _____

_____

What will happen to many of the people of the earth (19:17–18)? _____

_____

What will happen to the beast and the false prophet (19:20)? _____

_____

_____

What will happen to Satan (20:2–3)? _____
_____

What will Satan be powerless to do (20:3)? _____

How long will he be sealed in this way (20:3)? _____

What will happen to Satan after this period is over (20:3)? _____
_____

In our next lesson we will find out what will happen to Satan after he is set free.

Life During The Millennium

During the time Satan is chained in the Abyss, there will be a thousand years of peace on the earth. Christians will reign with Christ on the earth. There will be no war.

What does Habakkuk 2:14 say about why the earth will be filled with peace and joy during the Millennium? _____
_____
_____

The form of government and the way of life during the Millennium will be much different from what we are used to now. Satan will have no power. Christ will have complete control. The earth will be ruled as a theocracy.

Write the meaning of the word "theocracy." _____
_____

Read Jeremiah 23:5. What does this verse say about how Christ will rule the earth?
_____
_____

Life Principle: Christ knows how to rule in perfect love with perfect justice.

No human court or human judge can be perfect in these ways. With Christ ruling, the attitude on the earth will be very different. Out of love and justice, Christ will not allow wrong music, books, drugs, food, attitudes, etc., to destroy His reign over the earth.

To understand even more about what life will be like during this time, read Isaiah 2:2–4. Why will people go to the mountain of the Lord's temple? _____
_____

✎ What will the people do with their swords and spears? _____

_____

_____

✎ Why will they not need these instruments of war? _____

_____

✎ Even the animals will act differently than they do now. Describe how Isaiah says they will act (Is. 11:6–9). _____

_____

_____

Think what a wonderful place the earth will be when we return with the Lord and reign with Him and He executes what is just and right over all the earth. We should begin to praise the Lord now for the wonderful things He has planned for us in the future. Hallelujah! The Lord God Almighty reigns (Rev. 19:6).

Key Verse: Revelation 20:13

The Final Doom Of Satan

We have seen that conditions on the earth will be perfect during the Millennium. People will be dealt with in love and justice. There will be no wars or turmoil. The wicked will be dealt with immediately.

✎ During this time, remember, Satan has been bound. At the end of the Millennium, what will the Lord allow to happen (Rev. 20:7–8)? _____

_____

_____

Satan will again test the nations. During the Millennium, people who choose evil are not permitted to live. Now they are once again given a choice between God and Satan. It is difficult to believe, but after all the peace they have enjoyed on the earth, many will choose Satan's way once again when they are given a choice.

✎ There will not have been war on the earth for 1,000 years. What will happen when Satan is again free to work (Rev. 20:8–9)? _____

_____

✎ How will God deal with this (Rev. 20:9)? _____

_____

✎ According to Revelation 20:10, what will Satan's final destination be? _____

_____

✎ Will Satan ever be free again? _____

The Great White Throne Judgment

We have seen the final battle on the earth and the final and everlasting destruction of Satan. One last judgment is to be faced. This judgment will be for the unsaved. This judgment is called the Great White Throne Judgment. Christ will be the judge. All the unbelievers who have ever lived will be called forward to stand before Christ. They will all be judged according to what they have done. There will be no second chances to trust Christ because they will have already rejected Him.

Read Revelation 20:11–15 to find out what takes place at this final judgment.

Describe the judgment throne. _____

_____

How does John 5:22 let us know that Christ will be the one seated on this throne?

_____

_____

Who must stand before the Lord at this throne of judgment? _____

_____

What is the second death? _____

_____

Who must face the second death?_____

_____

Whose names are written in the Book of Life? _____

_____

What happens to those whose names are not found in the Book of Life? _____

_____

The long history of man on earth will end, and eternity will begin. And after this last judgment, the saved will dwell again with the Lord in a perfect place forever.

In Heaven For Eternity

There is no way we can ever really imagine how wonderful heaven will be. When we began our study of prophecy, we learned about heaven. Let us remind ourselves again of how it will be for us in eternity.

Read the following verses in Revelation 21 and write what heaven will be like:

- Verse 1: _____
  _____
  _____

- Verse 4: _____
  _____
  _____

- Verse 5: _____

- Verse 23: _____
  _____
  _____

- Verse 27: _____
  _____
  _____

We Shall See His Face

Revelation 22:4 tells us that when we as the Lord's servants are in heaven with Him, we will see His face. Imagine that you could see Christ face to face, and answer the following questions:

What would make you most excited? _____
_____
_____

What would you want to say to Him? _____
_____
_____

What would you wish could be different about how you spent your time and talents on earth? _____
_____
_____

Of what might you feel ashamed? _____
_____
_____

What do you think He would say to you? _____

_____

_____

Winning Your Race

Is your name written in the Book of Life? _____

How do you know this for sure? _____

_____

_____

Will you one day stand before God at the Judgment Seat of Christ? _____

Who will be judged there? _____

What is this judgment about? _____

Will you one day stand before God at the Great White Throne Judgment? _____

Who will be judged there? _____

What will happen to all those who will be judged there? _____

_____

Fill In The Blanks

 Use the words and phrases listed below to fill in the blanks.

Antichrist	lake of fire	eternal life	Millennium	King of kings
Rapture	Great White Throne	rewards	fire	wrath
1,000	Judgment Seat of Christ	future	Heaven	Tribulation

1. The Book of Revelation teaches us about _____ happenings.

2. The _____ is the "blessed hope" for all Christians.

3. Christians will one day stand before the _____,
    not to decide whether or not they will receive _____, but to have their
    works tried by the _____ of God's judgment. Those works which stand the test will be the
    basis for _____ given by God.

4. God has warned everyone in His Word about the coming day of His _____ on this earth,
    called the _____.

5. During this time a great world ruler, known as the _____, will appear.

6. After this period Christ will return to the earth as the _____.

7. Christ will then set up His kingdom on this earth and reign for _____ years.

8. The period of Christ's reign is known as the _____.

9. At the end of this period, all the unsaved will appear before the _____
    _____ judgment and will be thrown into the _____
    _____.

10. All who are saved will dwell with the Lord in _____ forever.

Multiple Choice

 Choose the best answer to complete each of the following statements:

1. In heaven there will be no _____.
   A. night
   B. mourning
   C. pain
   D. all of the above

2. It was prophesied by _____ that Israel and Judah would one day be restored to their homeland to possess it.
   A. Jeremiah
   B. Daniel
   C. John

3. God has promised to bless those who _____ the words of the Book of Revelation.
   A. read
   B. hear
   C. take to heart
   D. read, hear, and take to heart

4. Prophecy came to be written as men of God were carried along by _____.
   A. their imaginations
   B. the great events of history
   C. the Holy Spirit

5. Our bodies will be changed into a body like Christ's glorious body _____.
   A. at the Judgment Seat of Christ
   B. at the Rapture
   C. during the Millennium

6. We know we'll not be judged for sins at the Judgment Seat of Christ _____.
   A. because God has promised to remember them no more
   B. because we will be judged for our sins at the Great White Throne judgment
   C. because God is not interested in whether we sin or not

7. God wants our works as Christians to be like _____.
   A. gold, silver, costly stones
   B. wood, hay, straw

8. Daniel described the Tribulation as _____.
   A. the day of God's wrath
   B. a time of distress or trouble
   C. the day of Satan

9. During the Tribulation there will be _____ seal judgments.
   A. three
   B. seven
   C. ten

	10. The order of the Tribulation judgments will be as follows: _____.
	A. seals, bowls, trumpets **B.** trumpets, bowls, seals **C.** seals, trumpets, bowls
	11. During the Tribulation, _____ will be released from the bottomless pit (Abyss) to torment those without God's seal.
	A. birds **B.** locusts **C.** dragons
	12. Revelation 3:10 teaches us that _____.
	A. Christians will be kept from the Tribulation judgments **B.** the days of the Tribulation will be the worst the world has ever seen **C.** Satan will ultimately be defeated by God
	13. The Antichrist is also called the _____.
	A. Great Dragon **B.** Beast **C.** False Prophet
	14. One of the Tribulation judgments is that the _____ River will be dried up.
	A. Nile **B.** Jordan **C.** Euphrates
	15. In heaven faithful pastors will receive the crown of _____.
	A. life **B.** glory **C.** righteousness
	16. The battle that will occur at the Second Coming will be at a place called _____.
	A. Waterloo **B.** Jerusalem **C.** Armageddon
	17. During the Millennium, Satan will be bound in the _____.
	A. lake of burning sulfur **B.** bottomless pit (Abyss) **C.** holy city
	18. Which of the following will not occur during the Millennium?
	A. Nations will rise up to fight against each other. **B.** Christ will rule the earth by what is just and right. **C.** Wild animals will not harm people.
	19. Those who must face the second death are _____.
	A. those who were saved during the Millennium **B.** those whose names are not found in the book of life **C.** those who appear before the Judgment Seat of Christ.
	20. Revelation 22:4 teaches us that in heaven _____.
	A. we will see the Lord's face **B.** there will be no sun or moon **C.** there will be no death or mourning

Find The Chapter

 Find the following in the Book of Revelation and write in which chapter they are recorded:

	The first seal is opened.
	There is a half hour of silence in heaven.
	Christians are told that they will be kept from the hour of trial.
	One third of the ships are destroyed.
	Men are scorched by the sun.
	Christ appears with seven stars in His right hand.
	Christ returns from heaven on a white horse.
	Satan is bound for 1,000 years.
	The first trumpet is sounded.
	Men hide themselves in the caves and in the rocks of the mountains.
	John prays, "Come, Lord Jesus."
	Men need the mark of the beast in order to buy or sell.
	The first bowl is poured out.
	An ugly and painful sore breaks out on those with the mark of the beast.
	Birds eat the flesh of kings and horses.
	The holy city comes down from God out of heaven.

Seek And Find

 In the list of letters below, find the following words that occur in the Book of Revelation:

Alpha	Omega	Patmos	Mystery	Trumpet
Angel	Almighty	Lamb	Hades	Earthquake
Lightning	Beast	Zion	Glory	Judgment
Cursed	Bridegroom	Armageddon	Prison	Jerusalem

S S T X L E G N A H F P Q M T H N D D A

Q E T K X L Z B L I H W K S T S A E B A

P O D I L J E P M O I E U Y S T M R A B

E W Q A S U K S I D B F L O G E Y H R E

Y Y P O H D A K G N L M M L H N S I M B

T R V Z C G U X H Z O T Q P W E D E A R

H E T I Y M Q U T A A X S R I E L O G P

G T L O K E H A L P H A I I G J J B E H

I S G N I N T H G I L G M R N P M L D D

M Y O K N T R I J B A B O U P A H V D E

L M G C T M A F C R D O X G L O R Y O S

A G E M O O E A B C M D P R I S O N N R

F H G A B B T R U M P E T A N G L L E U

L A M E L A S U R E J B E A T S Z I O C

Music Curriculum

September Hymn

Jesus Paid It All

I hear the Savior say, "Thy strength indeed is small!
Child of weakness, watch and pray, find in Me thine all in all."

Lord, now indeed I find Thy pow'r, and Thine alone,
Can change the leper's spots and melt the heart of stone.

For nothing good have I whereby Thy grace to claim—
I'll wash my garments white in the blood of Calv'ry's Lamb.

And when before the throne I stand in Him complete,
"Jesus died my soul to save," my lips shall still repeat.

Chorus

Jesus paid it all, all to Him I owe;
Sin had left a crimson stain—He washed it white as snow.

September Choruses

Everybody Ought To Know

Ev'rybody ought to know
Ev'rybody ought to know
Ev'rybody ought to know who Jesus is.

He's the Lily of the Valley;
He's the bright and morning Star.
He's the Fairest of Ten Thousand,
Ev'rybody ought to know.

Ev'rybody ought to know
Ev'rybody ought to know
Ev'rybody ought to know who Jesus is.

O What He's Done For Me

Jesus loves me with a changeless love,
He to save me left His throne above;
All my sins He bore upon the tree;
I never can tell all He's done for me.

When I fell beneath a heavy load,
Faint and weary, on the downward road,
Jesus took me from the miry clay—
He led me into the King's highway.

I had sorrows that were hard to bear,
Heavy burdens that no soul could share;
When I fainted in my bitter grief,
He was the one came to my relief.

I'm so glad that Jesus is my friend,
His is friendship that will never end;
O that I could make the whole world see
Just what a Savior He is to me.

Chorus

O what He's done for me!
O what He's done for me!
If I tried to eternity,
I never could tell all He's done for me!

The Ninety And Nine

There were ninety and nine that safely lay
In the shelter of the fold,
But one was out on the hills away,
Far off from the gates of gold;
Away on the mountains wild and bare,
Away from the tender Shepherd's care,
Away from the tender Shepherd's care.

"Lord, Thou hast here Thy ninety and nine;
Are they not enough for Thee?"
But the Shepherd made answer: "This of Mine
Has wandered away from Me;
And although the road be rough and steep
I go to the desert to find My sheep,
I go to the desert to find My sheep."

But none of the ransomed ever knew
How deep were the waters crossed;
Or how dark was the night that the Lord passed thro'
Ere He found His sheep that was lost.
Out in the desert He heard its cry—
Sick and helpless, and ready to die,
Sick and helpless, and ready to die.

"Lord, whence are those blood drops all the way
That mark out the mountain's track?"
They were shed for one who had gone astray
Ere the Shepherd could bring him back.
"Lord, whence are Thy hands so rent and torn?"
"They're pierced tonight by many a thorn,
They're pierced tonight by many a thorn."

But all thro' the mountains, thunderriv'n,
And up from the rocky steep,
There rose a cry to the gate of heav'n,
"Rejoice! I have found My sheep!"
And the angels echoed around the throne,
"Rejoice, for the Lord brings back His own!
Rejoice, for the Lord brings back His own!"

October Hymn

Rock Of Ages

Rock of Ages, cleft for me, let me hide myself in Thee;
Let the water and the blood, from Thy riven side which flowed,
Be of sin the double cure, cleanse me from its guilt and pow'r.

Not the labors of my hands can fulfill Thy law's demands;
Could my zeal no respite know, could my tears forever flow,
All for sin could not atone; Thou must save and Thou alone.

Nothing in my hand I bring, simply to Thy cross I cling;
Naked, come to Thee for dress, helpless, look to Thee for grace;
Foul, I to the fountain fly, wash me, Savior, or I die!

While I draw this fleeting breath, when my eyes shall close in death,
When I soar to worlds unkown, see Thee on Thy judgment throne,
Rock of Ages, cleft for me, let me hide myself in Thee.

October Choruses

Some Golden Daybreak

Some golden daybreak Jesus will come;
Some golden daybreak, battles all won,
He'll shout the vict'ry, break thro' the blue,
Some golden daybreak, for me, for you.

Oh, How I Love Jesus

There is a name I love to hear,
I love to sing its worth;
It sounds like music in mine ear,
The sweetest name on earth.

It tells me of a Savior's love,
Who died to set me free;
It tells me of His precious blood;
The sinner's perfect plea.

It tells of One whose loving heart
Can feel my deepest woe,
Who in each sorrow bears a part,
That none can bear below.

Chorus

Oh, how I love Jesus,
Oh, how I love Jesus,
Oh, how I love Jesus
Because He first loved me.

Ye Must Be Born Again

A ruler once came to Jesus by night
To ask Him the way of salvation and light;
The Master made answer in words true and plain,
"Ye must be born again."

Ye children of men, attend to the word
So solemnly uttered by Jesus the Lord;
And let not this message to you be in vain,
"Ye must be born again."

O ye who would enter that glorious rest
And sing with the ransomed the song of the blest,
The life everlasting if ye would obtain,
"Ye must be born again."

Chorus

"Ye must be born again,
Ye must be born again;
I verily, verily say unto thee,
Ye must be born again."

November Choruses

I Am Feeding On The Living Bread

I am feeding on the living bread,
I am drinking at the fountain head;
And whoso drinketh, Jesus said,
Shall never, never thirst again.
(Boys) What, never thirst again?
(Girls) No! Never thirst again!
(Boys) What, never thirst again?
(Girls) No! Never thirst again!
(All) And whoso drinketh, Jesus said,
Shall never, never thirst again.

God Has Blotted Them Out

God has blotted them out,
I'm happy and glad and free;
God has blotted them out,
I'll turn to Isaiah and see;
Chapter forty-four,
Twenty-two and three;
He's blotted them out and now I can
shout,
For that means me.

No more am I in doubt,
His word is enough for me;
John three, verse thirty-six,
Has settled it all, you see;
How can I be sad,
When He makes me glad?
He's blotted them out, I'll sing and I'll
shout,
For He saves me.

Mansion Over The Hilltop

I'm satisfied with just a cottage below,
A little silver and a little gold;
But in that city where the ransomed will shine,
I want a gold one that's silver-lined.

Tho' often tempted, tormented and tested
And, like the prophet, my pillow a stone,
And tho' I find here no permanent dwelling,
I know He'll give me a mansion my own.

Don't think me poor or deserted or lonely—
I'm not discouraged, I'm heaven bound;
I'm just a pilgrim in search of a city,
I want a mansion, a harp and a crown.

Chorus
I've got a mansion just over the hilltop,
In that bright land where we'll never grow old;
And someday yonder we will never more wander,
But walk the streets that are purest gold.

December Hymn

Moment By Moment

Dying with Jesus by death reckoned mine,
Living with Jesus a new life divine,
Looking to Jesus till glory doth shine—
Moment by moment, O Lord, I am Thine.

Never a trial that He is not there,
Never a burden that He doth not bear;
Never a sorrow that He doth not share—
Moment by moment, I'm under His care.

Never a weakness that He doth not feel,
Never a sickness that He cannot heal;
Moment by moment, in woe or in weal,
Jesus, my Savior, abides with me still.

Chorus

Moment by moment I'm kept in His love,
Moment by moment I've life from above;
Looking to Jesus till glory doth shine,
Moment by moment, O Lord, I am Thine.

January Hymn

Softly And Tenderly

Softly and tenderly Jesus is calling, calling for you and for me;
See, on the portals He's waiting and watching, watching for you and for me.

Why should we tarry when Jesus is pleading, pleading for you and for me?
Why should we linger and heed not His mercies, mercies for you and for me?

Time is now fleeting, the moments are passing, passing from you and from me;
Shadows are gathering, death-beds are coming, coming for you and for me.

O for the wonderful love He has promised, promised for you and for me;
Tho' we have sinned He has mercy and pardon, pardon for you and for me.

Chorus

Come home, come home, ye who are weary, come home;
Earnestly, tenderly, Jesus is calling—calling, "O sinner, come home!"

January Choruses

How Blest Is The Man

How blest is the man who delights in the Lord,

Who walks in His counsel and honors His Word,
Who meditates daily in God's holy will,
And faithfully seeks His commands to fulfill.

Like a tree by the waters he stands straight and sure;
His leaf shall not wither, his strength shall endure!
Not so the ungodly who drift with the wind;
No peace for the present, no hope in the end.

The way of the righteous to God is well known—
One day they shall stand at His heavenly throne,
Forever to dwell in His presence on high,
While the godless, alas, in gross darkness must die!

Chorus

How blessed to walk in the ways of the Lord,
To feast on His goodness and follow His Word.
His step shall not falter, his strength shall endure.
Who follows the Lord is forever secure!

We Thank Thee, O Our Father

We thank Thee, O our Father,
For stories fine and true
Of people in the Bible
Who knew and loved Thee too.
They learned to serve Thee bravely,
To fight 'gainst sin and wrong.
They wondered at Thy goodness,
They praised Thee with a song.

We thank Thee, O our Father,
For stories fine and true
Of One who came so gladly,
His Father's work to do.
We like to hear of Jesus,
Who died on Calv'ry's tree.
We thank Thee for the Bible;
His story there we see.

Is It The Crowning Day?

Jesus may come today—
Glad day! Glad day!
And I would see my Friend;
Dangers and troubles would end
If Jesus should come today.

I may go home today—
Glad day! Glad day!
Seems like I hear their song:
Hail to the radiant throng
If I should go home today.

Faithful I'll be today—
Glad day! Glad day!
And I will freely tell
Why I should love Him so well,
For He is my all today.

Chorus

Glad day! Glad day!
Is it the crowning day?
I'll live for today, nor anxious be,
Jesus, my Lord, I soon shall see;
Glad day! Glad day!
Is it the crowning day?

February Hymn
Take My Life And Let It Be

Take my life and let it be consecrated, Lord, to Thee;
Take my moments and my days—let them flow in ceaseless praise,
Let them flow in ceaseless praise.

Take my hands and let them move at the impulse of Thy love;
Take my feet and let them be swift and beautiful for Thee,
Swift and beautiful for Thee.

Take my voice and let me sing always, only, for my King;
Take my lips and let them be filled with messages from Thee,
Filled with messages from Thee.

Take my silver and my gold—not a mite would I withhold;
Take my intellect and use ev'ry pow'r as Thou shalt choose,
Ev'ry pow'r as Thou shalt choose.

Take my will and make it Thine—it shall be no longer mine;
Take my heart—it is Thine own, it shall be Thy royal throne,
It shall be Thy royal throne.

Take my love—my Lord, I pour at Thy feet its treasure store;
Take my self—and I will be ever, only, all for Thee,
Ever, only, all for Thee.

February Choruses
Savior, Like A Shepherd Lead Us

Savior, like a shepherd lead us, much we need Thy tender care
In Thy pleasant pastures feed us, for our use Thy folds prepare:
Blessed Jesus, blessed Jesus, Thou hast bought us, Thine we are;
Blessed Jesus, blessed Jesus, Thou hast bought us, Thine we are.

We are Thine, do Thou befriend us, be the Guardian of our way;
Keep Thy flock, from sin defend us, seek us when we go astray:
Blessed Jesus, blessed Jesus, hear Thy children when they pray;
Blessed Jesus, blessed Jesus, hear Thy children when they pray.

Early let us seek Thy favor; early let us do Thy will;
Blessed Lord and only Savior, with Thy love our bosoms fill:
Blessed Jesus, blessed Jesus, Thou hast loved us, love us still;
Blessed Jesus, blessed Jesus, Thou hast loved us, love us still.

Singing Along The Way

Singing along in days of gladness,
Singing along the way the saints have trod,
Singing along in days of sadness,
Singing along the way with Christ my God.

Living For Jesus

Living for Jesus a life that is true,
Striving to please Him in all that I do,
Yielding allegiance, glad-hearted and free,
This is the pathway of blessing for me.

Living for Jesus who died in my place,
Bearing on Calv'ry my sin and disgrace,
Such love constrains me to answerHis call,
Follow His leading and give Him my all.

Living for Jesus wherever I am,
Doing each duty in His Holy Name,
Willing to suffer affliction or loss,
Deeming each trial a part of my cross.

Living for Jesus thro' earth's little while,
My dearest treasure, the light of His smile,
Seeking the lost ones He died to redeem,
Bringing the weary to find rest in Him.

Chorus

O Jesus, Lord and Savior,
I give myself to Thee;
For Thou, in Thy atonement,
Didst give Thyself for me;
I own no other Master,
My heart shall be Thy throne,
My life I give, henceforth to live,
O Christ, for Thee alone.

March Choruses

Isn't He Wonderful

Isn't He wonderful, wonderful, wonderful,
Isn't Jesus, my Lord, wonderful!
Eyes have seen, ears have heard,
'Tis recorded in God's Word,
Isn't Jesus, my Lord, wonderful.

Jesus Gave Her Water

Jesus gave her water that was not from the well,
Gave her living water, and sent her forth to tell;
She went away singing, and came back bringing
Others for the water that was not from the well.

A Child Of The King

My Father is rich in houses and lands,
He holdeth the wealth of the world in His hands!
Of rubies and diamonds, of silver and gold,
His coffers are full, He has riches untold.

My Father's own Son, the Savior of men,
Once wandered on earth as the poorest of them;
But now He is reigning forever on high,
And will give me a home in heav'n by and by.

I once was an outcast stranger on earth,
A sinner by choice, and an alien by birth;
But I've been adopted, my name's written down,
An heir to a mansion, a robe and a crown.

A tent or a cottage, why should I care?
They're building a palace for me over there;
Though exiled from home, yet still I may sing:
All glory to God, I'm a child of the King.

Refrain

I'm a child of the King, a child of the King:
With Jesus my Savior, I'm a child of the King.

April Hymn

The Love Of God

The love of God is greater far than tongue or pen can ever tell,
It goes beyond the highest star and reaches to the lowest hell;
The guilty pair, bowed down with care, God gave His Son to win:
His erring child He reconciled and pardoned from his sin.

When years of time shall pass away and earthly thrones and kingdoms fall,
When men, who here refuse to pray, on rocks and hills and mountains call,
God's love so sure shall still endure, all measureless and strong;
Redeeming grace to Adam's race—the saints' and angels' song.

Could we with ink the ocean fill and were the skies of parchment made,
Were ev'ry stalk on earth a quill and ev'ry man a scribe by trade,
To write the love of God above would drain the ocean dry,
Nor could the scroll contain the whole tho' stretched from sky to sky.

Chorus

O love of God, how rich and pure! How measureless and strong!
It shall forevermore endure—the saints' and angels' song.

April Choruses

Stand Fast For Christ

Stand fast for Christ thy Savior, stand fast whate'er betide;
Keep thou the faith, unstained, unshamed, by keeping at His side;
Be faithful, ever faithful, where'er thy lot be cast,
Stand fast for Christ, stand fast for Christ, stand faithful to the last.

Stouthearted like a soldier, who never leaves the fight,
But meets the foeman face to face and meets him with his might;
So bear thee in thy battles until the war be past,
Stand fast for Christ, stand fast for Christ, stand faithful to the last.

Stand fast for Christ thy Savior; He once stood fast for thee;
And standeth still, and still shall stand for all eternity:
Be faithful, oh, be faithful, to love so true, so vast,
Stand fast for Christ, stand fast for Christ, stand faithful to the last.

In The Sweet By And By

In the sweet by and by,
In the sweet by and by
I have a mansion so bright and so fair;
Won't it be glorious when I get there?
In the sweet by and by,
In the sweet by and by,
When the battle is done and the vict'ry is won,
In the sweet by and by.

Surely Goodness And Mercy

A pilgrim was I, and a wond'ring—
In the cold night of sin I did roam
When Jesus the kind Shepherd found me—
And now I am on my way home.

He restoreth my soul when I'm weary,
He giveth me strength day by day;
He leads me beside the still waters,
He guards me each step of the way.

When I walk thru the dark lonesome valley,
My Savior will walk with me there;
And safely His great hand will lead me
To the mansions He's gone to prepare.

Chorus

Surely goodness and mercy shall follow me
All the days, all the days of my life;
Surely goodness and mercy shall follow me
All the days, all the days of my life.

(May be omitted until final chorus)

And I shall dwell in the house of the Lord forever,
And I shall feast at the table spread for me;
Surely goodness and mercy shall follow me
All the days, all the days of my life,
All the days, all the days of my life.

May Hymn

At Calvary

Years I spent in vanity and pride,
Caring not my Lord was crucified,
Knowing not it was for me He died
On Calvary.

By God's Word at last my sin I learned—
Then I trembled at the law I'd spurned,
Till my guilty soul imploring turned
To Calvary.

Now I've giv'n to Jesus ev'rything,
Now I gladly own Him as my King,
Now my raptured soul can only sing
Of Calvary.

O the love that drew salvation's plan!
O the grace that bro't it down to man!
O the mighty gulf that God did span
At Calvary!

Chorus

Mercy there was great and grace was free,
Pardon there was multiplied to me,
There my burdened soul found liberty—
At Calvary.

May Choruses

There Was A Brave Soldier Named Gideon

There was a brave soldier named Gideon,
Who won a great fight against Midian.
Tho' his army was small,
He conquered them all.
He trusted the Lord, don't you see?
The lesson we learn from this story
Is to trust in the Lord ev'ry day.
Then tho' Satan assail us,
Our God will not fail us,
But keep us each step of the way.

Take More Time To Pray

Take more time to pray.
Take more time to pray.
The world's in such a hurry,
Hearts are filled with fear.
Trust the Savior, He's always near.
Take more time to pray.
Take more time to pray.
Tho' cares may surround you,
They need not confound you;
Take more time to pray.

He Keeps Me Singing

There's within my heart a melody—
Jesus whispers sweet and low,
"Fear not, I am with thee—peace, be still,"
In all of life's ebb and flow.

All my life was wrecked by sin and strife,
Discord filled my heart with pain;
Jesus swept across the broken strings,
Stirr'd the slumb'ring chords again.

Feasting on the riches of His grace,
Resting 'neath His shelt'ring wing,
Always looking on His smiling face—
That is why I shout and sing.

Tho' sometimes He leads thru waters deep,
Trials fall across the way,
Tho' sometimes the path seems rough and steep,
See His footprints all the way.

Soon He's coming back to welcome me
Far beyond the starry sky;
I shall wing my flight to worlds unknown,
I shall reign with Him on high.

Chorus

Jesus, Jesus, Jesus—sweetest name I know,
Fills my ev'ry longing, keeps me singing as I go.

Winning The Race Scripture Memorization Report Sheet

Name:_____ Grade:_____ Teacher:_____

Week	Scripture	Due Date	Parent's Signature
1	Matt. 5:1–3		
2	Matt. 5:4–6		
3	Matt. 5:7–9		
4	**Matt. 5:1–9**		
5	Matt. 5:10–12		
6	Matt. 5:13–14		
7	Matt. 5:15–16		
8	**Matt. 5:10–16**		
9	Rom. 8:28–30		
10	Rom. 8:31–32		
11	Rom. 8:33–34		
12	Rom. 8:35–37		
13	Rom. 8:38–39		
14	**Rom. 8:28–39**		
15	Prov. 3:1–2		
16	Prov. 3:3–4		
17	Prov. 3:5–6		
18	**Prov. 3:1–6**		
19	Prov. 3:7–8		
20	Prov. 3:9–10		
21	Prov. 3:11–12		
22	**Prov. 3:7–12**		
23	1 Thess. 4:13–14		
24	1 Thess. 4:15–16		
25	1 Thess. 4:17–18		
26	**1 Thess. 4:13–18**		
27	James 1:1–2		
28	James 1:3–4		
29	James 1:5–6		
30	James 1:7–8		
31	**James 1:1–8**		
32	John 14:1–2		
33	John 14:3–4		
34	John 14:5–7		
35	**John 14:1–7**		